"You Want Me to Pack My Bags and Go?"

he asked incredulously. "Never darken your door again?"

"Yes."

"After everything we've felt for each other?"

"Yes."

"I see. Just leave without any fuss. Goodbye, it's been fun." His voice was bitter. Suddenly his hand clamped down on her shoulder. "This doesn't make any sense! We have something special. We shouldn't leave it now."

"What do we have, J.T.? Do you love me, or do you just love to make love to me?"

The room rang with his silence as he struggled to find an answer.

RITA CLAY

has tried almost every job once. This former bookstore manager also sold cosmetics, worked in a bank and ran her own modeling school before turning to writing. Now a successful romance author, she looks forward to describing the diversity and joys of love in many books to come.

Dear Reader:

SILHOUETTE DESIRE is an exciting new line of contemporary romances from Silhouette Books. During the past year, many Silhouette readers have written in telling us what other types of stories they'd like to read from Silhouette, and we've kept these comments and suggestions in mind in developing SILHOUETTE DESIRE.

DESIREs feature all of the elements you like to see in a romance, plus a more sensual, provocative story. So if you want to experience all the excitement, passion and joy of falling in love, then SILHOUETTE DESIRE is for you.

I hope you enjoy this book and all the wonderful stories to come from SILHOUETTE DESIRE. I'd appreciate any thoughts you'd like to share with us on new SILHOUETTE DESIRE, and I invite you to write to us at the address below:

Karen Solem
Editor-in-Chief
Silhouette Books
P.O. Box 769
New York, N.Y. 10019

RITA CLAY
Summer Song

Silhouette Desire
Published by Silhouette Books New York
America's Publisher of Contemporary Romance

Other Silhouette Books by Rita Clay

Wanderer's Dream
Wise Folly
Sweet Eternity
Yesterday's Dreams
Experiment in Love

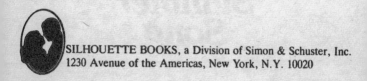

SILHOUETTE BOOKS, a Division of Simon & Schuster, Inc.
1230 Avenue of the Americas, New York, N.Y. 10020

ISBN: 0-671-44374-7

First Silhouette Books printing August, 1983

10 9 8 7 6 5 4 3 2 1

America's Publisher of Contemporary Romance

Printed in the U.S.A.

For the real Summer,
my Meagan Marie Holt,
and
for a talented editor who cares,
Leslie Wainger

Summer
Song

1

I won't allow my brother to hire himself out as a stud!" A large fist banged down on the wide antique desk top. "I don't care how many contracts he signs!"

The young, well-dressed attorney behind the desk watched his friend's anger with sympathetic eyes, realizing just how much of a shock this was. "Calm down, J.T., and let me explain the rest of the agreement to you. Maybe you'll change your mind. I promised Brandon I'd give it a try, anyway."

The man called J.T. took an exasperated breath before sitting down in the red leather chair closest to the desk. His hands were clenched into fists at his sides, his mouth tight with anger. He was a rugged, masculine man, perhaps too much so to be handsome. Certainly the right features were all there: deep brown eyes that could turn soft when he looked at women but would be rock-hard when he dealt with business associates; thick, dark hair that was layered to fall back in perfect but casual symmetry. His nose had been broken once or twice, although that only seemed to add to his sex appeal. To clinch his attractiveness, his broad shoulders, trim hips, and muscular thighs were dead giveaways to the fact that he was in peak physical condition. He was two or three inches under six feet, but that didn't seem to matter to anyone, including six-foot-tall women. He was dynamite, and all women seemed to sense it.

"There's nothing you can tell me, Mike, that will make me change my decision. This girl can take her money and go find another stud to fill her needs. Why is she going this route, anyway? Why can't she just go find some guy willing to bed her and leave kids young enough to still be in school alone?"

"First of all, Caro Halter is not some deviant who's looking for a thrill," Mike answered patiently. "And your brother is now twenty-one years old and capable of answering for and to himself, contrary to your family's opinion. Caro is looking for a man with the right genes who can give her a child. Period. She doesn't want anyone to come back to her or to the child ten years from now and say, 'Remember me?' Thus the money and the contract."

"And my brother is the only guy who fills these qualifications, I suppose." J.T. snorted derisively. "I don't buy it."

"You don't have to. Brandon is old enough to make up his own mind, which he did." Mike waited for the fireworks to flare. He wasn't disappointed.

"I say no! Brandon isn't old enough to tie his own shoes, for God's sake! This job is probably the only thing he's had experience doing, but that doesn't mean he can't learn something else! And he wouldn't have told me about it if he hadn't wanted me to help him get out of this situation. He's scared and he's gotten himself in over his head, that's all.'' His brown eyes narrowed. "How do you know this girl won't try to blackmail him years from now? Or accuse the rest of the family of not sharing responsibility? What kind of girl would 'hire' someone for a job like this?''

"She's a respected member of the community and a very successful businesswoman. She's attractive, talented, and very reserved. As for her reasons, I think she's always wanted children but never found anyone she wanted to marry. Adoption is out of the question. Even married couples have a problem with adoption today, but single parents have it even rougher. As for her trying to contact Brandon in the future, I think it's obvious that she's more worried about him finding her.''

"If this gal's so great, why don't you apply for the job yourself?'' J.T. growled over his shoulder as he stood and walked to the far window to stare out. "Seems like the perfect solution to me, since you seem so taken with the idea.''

"I know too much about Caro for her to be comfortable. She's been a client of mine for the last five years. She's worth ten of Brandon and, despite our long friendship, two of you. If I could have persuaded her to do otherwise, I would have, believe me.''

J.T. was silent for a moment. When he looked back at his friend, his eyes were glimmering with new purpose. "What about me? If Brandon qualifies, then I certainly must. What would happen if I took Brandon's place in this fiasco?"

Mike shrugged, not realizing that his friend's question was a ploy to gain more information about the girl. Worry etched his forehead. "If you wish to meet with her, I can arrange it. However, she's meeting with Brandon this afternoon." He stared down at the unopened folder in front of him. "I don't want you to think there's something wrong with this woman, J.T. There isn't. She's intelligent, witty, and beautiful. Only her means to an end are being discussed here, not her morals or ethics, which are far above standard."

J.T. made a choking noise deep in his throat. "I think anyone could sell you anything if it was wrapped up nice enough. Apparently this girl has pretty paper and her ribbons are in the right places. That doesn't mean the contents are top quality."

"It does in this case." Mike was stubborn. "This woman isn't like most. She's different."

J.T. stood. "We'll see." His determination to expose the woman was almost as strong as his desire to stop his brother from participating in this crazy scheme. And now there was the added bonus of proving to Mike just how faulty his character judgement was . . . again.

He could get Brandon out of the contract, there was no problem there. But the challenge of the situation was just too strong to be turned down. He would try to persuade her to do things his way; then, when the time was right and before any harm was done, he would walk away, leaving her high and dry. She would lose, Mike would lose, and he would get Brandon out of a scrape in a way that might prove entertaining.

J.T. Cole walked out of the plush law offices of his boyhood friend, practically marched to the elevators, and jabbed the down button.

Thoughts seared through his brain with lightning-fast speed. His mother would be crushed by Brandon's behavior, despite the fact that she had made him the spoiled youngest child of the Cole family. His other three brothers would have very different reactions, ranging from haughty anger to snickering approval. But it was his father he was really worried about. His father had a tricky heart, as had been proven time and again by small attacks after every one of Brandon's escapades. This latest problem, coming as a total surprise to the rest of the family and involving the one thing their family held dear—children—could do their father enough harm to provoke a major attack.

Damn that Brandon!

Five sons and one daughter were the firm foundation of the Cole family. One word could best be used to describe them—they were all overachievers . . . except for Brandon. In earlier days Brandon had been laughingly referred to as "Brandon the Lazy," for if he thought there was a way to make money without working, Brandon would work twice as hard at it as any legitimate job would have demanded to achieve that goal.

J.T. stepped aboard the elevator when the doors

finally opened. The funny side of the situation was beginning to make itself known. His anger had even simmered down enough to let him appreciate the insinuating looks of the two secretaries who were traveling down to street level with him. Before he stepped off he gave each of them a warm smile, showing to advantage the curl of his upper lip and the fullness of his mouth.

It would work out. He'd play her along, like he had often done with catfish on the hook when he went fishing. Mike had inadvertently disclosed the hotel she had chosen to stay at, which should make her easy to find, since single women staying there weren't that plentiful. It should be simple to spot her, especially if he could get a description of her from Brandon. Brandon was always easy to pump for answers, perhaps because he had always been re-warded for giving them. And right now he wanted out of this situation. He must, or he wouldn't finally have "confessed" to J.T.

Suddenly J.T. felt like whistling. He had almost forgotten that he had a date to take Candice out that night. She was easy on the eye but undemanding enough to allow him to think of other, more impor-tant things while he entertained her. Perhaps he'd take her to the Utah Hotel for dinner. . . .

Caro's first thought after she walked through the heavy glass doors of Salt Lake City's most famous hotel was that he looked so young! She quickly scanned the plush lobby, searching for some other young man in faded jeans and an even more faded green knit shirt who could fit the description her attorney had given her, but there was no one else who looked even remotely similar.

He was slumped against one of the huge gray marble pillars, looking like an imitation of Samson holding up the entire mezzanine with his slim but athletic body. His expression showed him to be filled with both worry and youthful impatience.

She took a deep breath and approached him, knowing that her calm exterior would hide her nervousness. "Brandon Cole?" she questioned. Standing before him in her tottery high heels she came, just barely, to the level of his broad shoulders. She held out her hand, determined to keep control of the interview. "I'm Carolyn." His young face was blank, with only a flicker of interest in his pale brown eyes to show that he even noticed the petite but intensely feminine woman standing in front of him. "I'm the person you came here to meet," she reminded him with a touch of dryness in her tone. He flushed a dull red, standing straighter instead of slouching, suddenly showing the uneasiness she had expected all along.

His hand was cold and clammy, his clasp weak. Not good, but not an inherited trait. She turned and scanned the lobby for a private conversational area, and found one immediately.

"Shall we sit over here?" She guided him to the spot she had selected. Was she going to have to guide him every step of the way? She hoped not! She wasn't that familiar with the ways of sin herself!

He gestured nervously, the sweep of his hand encompassing the entire lobby, with its marble, its plush red-velvet draperies, and its Persian carpets. It was the oldest hotel in Salt Lake City and certainly one of the finest, almost as revered a landmark as the Mormon Temple and grounds across the street.

"Beautiful hotel." His voice was an octave higher than it had sounded on the telephone earlier.

"Yes, it is, isn't it?" Perhaps he needed a little time to get his bearings. "Did you bring the papers from Dr. Sanders?"

He reached into the back pocket of his faded jeans, pulled out a folded sheet of paper, and offered it to her, his eyes lighting on her face for the first time since they had introduced themselves. His eyes seemed to take in her appearance all at once. Her dark golden-blond hair was loose, hanging in waves to her shoulders and framing her oval face. Her silvery brown eyes were delicately tinted with the same color eye shadow, making her seem slightly mysterious. Her figure, although she was small in stature, was perfectly formed.

"Why are you doing this?" He sounded perplexed, inquisitive. "You're good-looking, for an older woman. You certainly have more going for you than most of the girls I know. Charm, polish, a sexy body. Any guy'd be crazy not to want to fall into bed with you. Why me?"

She mentally winced at his crudeness. The paper remained folded on her lap for a moment while she took another deep breath. He deserved an answer. Besides, he might as well know now, since it looked as if he was her best choice.

She ignored her own trepidation. After all her hours of intense soul-searching, this was the only answer she had come up with. It didn't matter that she had doubts herself. It was the end result that mattered most. She would finally have a family to call her own.

"First of all, this is to be done by artificial insemination, so no one has to 'fall into bed' with anyone. But, to answer the rest of your question, I'm thirty-five years old and I've decided I want a child without the encumbrance of a husband. I also want a bright child, free of inherited illness. If I find the right male surrogate I've eliminated whatever problems that I can for the sake of the child." Her smile was bright and brittle, hiding her own indecision. She had made her choice and now she was moving to carry it out.

"And I'm it?" A smirk suddenly appeared on his face, but it wasn't inherited, either. It came from being young and virile and good-looking in a society that paid too much attention to such things and not enough to the qualities that lay underneath a handsome shell.

"We don't know that yet, do we?" She eyed him with an even gaze that had intimidated businessmen more than once. His smirk washed away, to be replaced with a dull flush. Her hands were unfolding the paper even before she glanced down. She scanned the printed words. Yes, he was in perfect health; yes, he was male and over twenty-one . . . barely. Yes, he had had the usual childhood diseases but none of the debilitating ones that could be inherited. Neither, apparently, had his parents, four brothers, and one sister. Everything was in order.

Now came the questions. In a very businesslike tone Caro began requesting, even demanding, the answers she wanted.

"Do you need the fee I'll be paying you for your services?"

"Yes." His voice turned sullen.

"Why?"

"I want to open a ski shop."

"Where?" Her voice sharpened and she leaned forward.

"In Snowhawk." He named one of the better-known ski slopes.

"If I upped the ante, would you consider moving to another state? Perhaps Colorado?"

His light brown eyes lit up with interest. "Why?" It was his turn to ask questions.

"Because I live in Utah and I would prefer that you didn't."

"Does that mean I have the 'job'?" His grin turned into another smirk as he studied her slim body, obviously seeing her naked in his mind.

His crude ploy made her blood boil. He could use being taken down a peg! "It means that I'm still considering the remote possibility." Her tone quelled him. "I'm not ready to hand over thousands of dollars to someone just because he has a nice, undiseased body. If that were the case, I would never have gotten to the point of interviewing you."

He winced. "Ouch, lady."

"Think nothing of it." She contained the grin that threatened to curve her lips and show off her deep dimples.

He sighed, leaning back in the low red velvet chair. "Okay. What now?" His lounging form reminded her so much of a typical teenager that she almost wished she had cancelled this appointment. But he had all the qualifications and, just as important, no visible bad habits. Still . . .

"Now we both think about it." She stood, all five feet three of her, and eyed him much as a mother would. "What does your family have to say about this? Have you discussed this with them?"

"Lord, no!" He stood, unwinding his lean frame from its casual position to tower over her.

She tilted her head sideways, staring up at him and wondering how long it would be before she got a crick in her neck. "Why not?"

"Well, I did tell my sister, but she thinks I'm crazy anyway." His grin told her that he liked his sister. His easy stance told her that he had suddenly relaxed as he began to talk about his family. That was a good sign.

Caro glanced down at the physician's form. "And did you mention this to any of your brothers?"

"No." Brandon's voice turned low and flat and she looked up in surprise. "This has nothing to do with them."

"I would think that this was just the sort of thing a bunch of men would talk about. After all, a man being hired—"

"What I do is my business," he interrupted firmly, showing a streak of determination that she hadn't guessed he possessed. She was pleased.

"And how will you feel three, five, ten years from now? Do you think you'll have an urge to see the child you created?"

He shrugged. "Why should I? I imagine there are a

lot of guys who go through life wondering if they've fathered any little brats along the way. I'll bet it drives them nuts, haunting them." He grinned. "This way I'll know for sure, and I'll also know that you won't let my secret out or allow any noble motives to get in the way when the kid gets big and wants to find his real parents."

Caro's voice hardened. "I'll *be* the 'real parents.' Make no mistake, this is my baby. You'll just be a man with some extra money in his pocket."

"Fair enough," he said. "When will I know your decision?"

"I'll have my attorney call you by the end of the week." She saw the gleam that immediately entered his eyes and quelled it with her next words. "In the meantime I'll decide if I think we're compatible. If I do, then we'll discuss the next step."

"I still have to work for a living, you know," he countered.

"So do I," she answered, holding out her hand to demonstrate that the interview was over. "We'll be in touch. Thank you for your time."

The skirt of her silk dress swished against her sleek, nylon-encased legs as she turned and retraced her steps out the front door and stepped into a taxi. She never looked back, never waved, never saw that Brandon Cole watched her with narrowed eyes and an expression wiser than his youth. She didn't see the calculated look that passed fleetingly over his face before it was quickly hidden from passing guests.

The cab drove around the city, following her

instructions. They passed the gold-domed state capitol and the high-walled Mormon Temple grounds. Caro gave Brandon Cole plenty of time to leave the hotel. Finally the driver stopped in a side street, allowing her to use another entrance to the hotel. Her steps were muffled by the carpeted hallway as she took a sharp right and pushed the elevator button. If he was still waiting in the lobby, he would wait a long time. If he asked the desk clerk for her room number, he would be told there was no "Carolyn" registered under any last name. Everything that could be done to retain her mysterious identity had been done. There would be no way for him to trace her, either then or later.

She opened the door to her suite and immediately slipped off her shoes, then stripped off her dress and slip. What she needed was a hot bath and a few hours of sleep before tackling any decision-making.

Her warm shower was soothing rather than invigorating. The triple-sheeted bed made Caro smile. Where else would one find a bottom sheet, top sheet and a sheeted blanket except in the finest hotels? Certainly not at home. She grinned, eyes closed and hand sensuously rubbing the top sheet, feeling the softness of the pristine material. She didn't travel from home often, but when she did it was marvelous to know that she could finally afford to go first class. Her mind was fuzzy with impending sleep and she felt as if she were floating in midair in the quiet room.

She thought over her conversation with Brandon Cole, and his knowing, cocky manner. She had met many men of his type during her years of traveling with a band. He and the others like him had the one thing she had always craved: family. And he didn't even know how lucky he was! What a waste of such a valuable asset.

All her life Caro had dreamed of having a family, someone to call her own. Even knowing that families had their share of problems and conflicts hadn't detracted from her teenage daydreams in which she was loved and cared for by parents, sisters, and brothers. She longed for someone who would love her despite her faults. Once she had thought that her dreams of a home and husband were about to come true, only to find that the call of his family was stronger than his attraction to her. And when his family pressured him to give up his role as lead guitarist in the band that he and Caro had formed and come home to marry his childhood sweetheart, he had done so, strengthening her original theory that blood was always thicker than water. It was then that she had taken off the blindfold that love had tied over her eyes and she had never replaced it.

Life had taught her a hard lesson and she had remembered it well. Caro wasn't masochistic enough to try love again. In fact, she consistently withdrew from anything that remotely resembled an entanglement. Everything and everyone, with the exception of Sam, her general manager and surrogate father. But his love, although sorely needed and appreciated, wasn't enough. Although loving someone else had been so painful an ordeal that she'd shied away from it ever since, something was missing. Yet she'd never regretted the direction her life had taken, had she? She shoved her doubts aside. This was the path she had chosen and that was that. Slowly her eyes closed and she slept.

The noise seemed to fit into her dream at first; then suddenly it pricked her unconscious enough to make her wake up. It was the phone.

"Yes?" Her voice was clipped and assured, but her mind was still wrapped in cotton gauze.

"Caro, I'm just checking in with you before the evening crowd starts storming the doors. Everything going all right?"

She grinned. "Yes, Sam, everything's fine. The final interview is over and I'm just going to have dinner in the dining room before relaxing with a good book."

"No company to entertain you?" Sam's gravelly voice sounded teasing as he covered his concern.

"I'm by myself, Sam," she promised. "I'm not doing anything I'm not supposed to. In fact, I'm enjoying the fact that I'm not working. This has turned into a holiday."

Caro could hear musical instruments tuning up in the background, letting her know that Sam was using the bar phone instead of the one in the office. His rough Western twang grew louder.

"Well, I was just checkin'. I didn't want any surprises when I picked you up tomorrow."

"No surprises," she said firmly. "Was there any trouble last night?"

"Nope. And the take was good. I'll show you the receipts when you get back. We had a group in here from San Jose last night. They were loud but harmless." Sam's voice held a hint of laughter. That was what he liked best, a loud, but fun, group. It made the already excellent reputation of The Loose Noose bar and dance hall spread faster and farther than advertising could ever do.

"Good deal. I'll see you tomorrow afternoon. Two o'clock. Don't forget."

"I won't. Just you be ready, little lady," he admonished her, as he would a child. "And don't be late. Some of us have to work for a living!"

She chuckled. "I'll be ready."

The hotel restaurant was one of the finest in Utah. Caro was shown to her seat by a waiter who had obviously been with them for years. He knew many of the customers by name, and she suspected that he could read the labels of the clothing of those he didn't know. There was no random selection of seating; everyone was seated according to wealth, class, or social station.

Obviously her midnight-black designer dress and sleekly pulled-back hairdo put her in the "upper-class" section. He found a small table cozily situated in the corner of the room for her. It was perfect. She ordered quickly and competently, requesting a half-bottle of dry white wine to accompany her broiled filet of sole smothered with thinly sliced walnuts. Almost immediately the waiter returned, deftly pouring her wine to allow her to approve the taste, then filling her glass with the golden liquid.

She gave a contented sigh and sat back, perusing the room. Her second favorite thing to do was people watching. Her first was watching her club grow in prestige and profitability. Luckily, one gave her the opportunity for the other. Her club, The Loose Noose, had been in existence for seven years, over five of them under her ownership. It wasn't often that she left Park City and the club to come into Salt Lake City, so this trip was truly a treat. People came to Park City to vacation and have fun. Skiing, drinking, and kicking up booted heels were the order of the day. But Salt Lake City people were businessmen and women relaxing quietly after a hard day's work.

Her eyes were drawn to the table across from her. A young, dark-haired woman laughed throatily at her escort, one beringed hand stroking the top of his wrist, her fingertips lazily outlining the circular gold face of his very expensive watch. Her brown eyes promised untold delights; her mouth pouted in readiness to be kissed. The man himself listened to her with tolerant amusement etched on his roughly hewn face. His thick, dark brows met across his forehead in a frown at something she said, his full, carved lips thinning as he shook his head in answer to her obvious pleading. Caro had the feeling that most women would have been put off if a man changed temperament as quickly as he seemed to have done, but it didn't seem to daunt his date in the slightest. Caro grinned. Women were such fools to play into a man's hands like that! Thank goodness that childish part of her life was behind her and she could see men for what they were: necessary if the business world was to continue spinning, but totally unnecessary emotionally for any intelligent woman.

The man in question looked up to lock eyes with Caro, scanning her face and form before nodding in both acknowledgement and silent invitation. An intangible chill ran up her spine at the intimacy of his look, making her totally aware of his masculinity. Her lips pursed in disapproval. He had his hands full with one woman and yet he really thought he could handle another. Some men's egos knew no bounds!

She paid her bill with a credit card, gathered her purse and shawl, and left the darkened restaurant. As usual, she ignored the appreciative male eyes watching her progress across the room, especially those of the dark-browed man. It was time to get a good night's sleep before calling the doctor and attorney to verify the information that the young man had given her.

Caro fell asleep with an easy conscience, dreaming of a lovely, golden-haired child who called her Mother.

Early the next morning everything was packed, all her calls made, and Caro was ready to leave, anxious to see her own home again. She'd been gone for three days, plenty of time for her to see the world before running back to the cozy nest she had built for herself. Her nest meant security, money, roots. With one exception, she had attained everything she had ever wanted as a child, having worked hard and long to ensure her success. She knew she was lucky. Some people never achieved the degree of security she had.

The telephone rang.

"Yes?" Her voice was cool, businesslike. No one in Salt Lake City knew she was in town.

"Miss Carolyn?" A deep voice with a slight southern drawl sped over the line.

"Yes." There was no point in explaining that that was her first name.

"I'm calling about Brandon Cole. I'd like to meet with you and discuss the arrangement you've made with him." His voice was briskly direct, his manner cold and arrogant.

"I'm sorry, but anything you wish to discuss should be done with him. I don't believe any of this is your business." She was equally brisk.

"Anything to do with Brandon is my business."

"And who are you?"

"That doesn't matter." He brushed her words aside. "I want to terminate this arrangement he has with you."

"Have you told him that?"

"I'm telling you."

"Since I haven't chosen a candidate yet, I suggest you wait to see if he is even chosen."

"My God, you mean there are others?" His voice was dry with sarcasm.

"It's really none of your business." Without waiting for him to speak again, Caro quietly hung up the phone.

She didn't like that. She didn't like it at all. Only the two people who were involved should discuss something like this. Damn! Yesterday she had asked that young man if he had discussed the issue with his brothers and he had said no. Did that mean he was lying, or that he had talked to someone else? Her curiosity was piqued, but she didn't have time to think about it right then. It was time to go. The doubts that had originally assailed her came to the fore, but she shoved them back, shaking off the uneasy feeling the call had elicited. The telephone began to ring again but this time Caro ignored it.

She placed her two matching tan suitcases by the door, glancing around to make sure that she hadn't forgotten anything. Quickly she walked to the bathroom, scanning the counters and floor. Something in the corner glittered a dull gold. It was one of the large hooped earrings a friend had given her for her birthday the year before. Seeing it, however, was easier than getting it. It was wedged between the counter top and the commode, and Caro could barely reach it.

"What I need is a five-foot-long arm as thin as a mop handle," she muttered before remembering that she had heard the cleaning women out in the hall earlier. Surely she would have a mop Caro could use to reach the earring.

Within minutes she had used the mop handle to do just that, while the small, dark maid stood behind her, watching as Caro carefully attempted to edge the earring within touching distance.

"Anything I can do to help?" The slow southern drawl echoed off the tile walls.

Both Caro and the maid jumped, and Caro dropped the mop handle with a clatter.

"Look what you made me do!" Her heart was

beating a fast tattoo, her breathing irregular, as she glared at the man standing in the bathroom doorway. It took a minute for her mind to register the fact that he was the same rugged man she had seen in the restaurant the evening before. He was wearing a pale gray suit with a white silk shirt and a ruby and azure tie. Every inch the gentleman. But his face was rugged and rough, contrasting with his smooth appearance. His build was muscular and his feet-apart stance reminded her of someone at the helm of a ship. His features were hard, carved, and slightly uneven in a sensuously masculine way.

"I'll reach it," he promised, shrugging out of his jacket and tossing it on the bed before placing his hands on the maid's waist and moving her aside, then doing the same to Caro.

She didn't say a word, letting the expression in her dark eyes speak volumes as she ungraciously moved, hoping that he couldn't reach the earring. But he could. He held it up, displaying his catch with a grin that probably would have melted the heart of a more susceptible woman.

The grinning maid slipped out of the room, mop in tow, and shut the door behind her.

"Thank you," Caro said with just a touch of defiance and a slightly tilted chin.

"I'm sure you're welcome." His grin continued to light up his face as he conspicuously mapped out the pliant curves of her body before staring at the rose of her cheeks and the flash of anger that emanated from her deep, silver-brown eyes.

She motioned him out of the confines of the

cramped bathroom and toward the less intimate bedroom. He grinned broadly as if reading her mind, then followed her to sit on the bed as if he had been invited for the night.

"Is there something you want?" she asked in her sternest voice. People at The Loose Noose would have recognized it as the tone she used just before she called the sheriff's office. However, this man didn't realize just how close he was to unleashing her temper.

"I came to speak to you," he said, studying the length and shape of her slim legs. "I want to offer you a deal."

"I'm afraid I don't understand. What sort of deal?" Her arms were crossed in front of her in an attempt to hide the womanly attributes he had begun to study in detail. But in crossing her arms she had unknowingly accented the fullness of her breasts by tightening the material of the blue silk blouse that covered them.

"If you drop this 'proposition' with Brandon Cole I won't be forced to file charges for prostitution." The humor had fled. His voice was quiet, with just a hint of a southern drawl, but his eyes were as hard as polished brown pebbles.

Caro clenched her hands to keep them from shaking with anger and a fear she didn't want to admit. "Get out," she said quietly.

He didn't move off the bed. "If it's sex you want, then I know a few hundred men who would be willing to oblige. If it's a baby you want, there are orphanages." His voice lowered to a gravelly rasp. "And if it's trouble you want, then continue on this

course. I warn you now, I'm not letting this go any
further."

"If you have any more to say, please say it to my
attorney, Mr. Mike Avery, here in Salt Lake City."

For just a fraction of a second there was a glint of
admiration in his dark brown eyes. Then it was
hooded. "And who shall I say his client is? Miss
Carolyn? I doubt it."

"You could use that name and glean the proper
information." She turned slowly, reaching for her
purse at the foot of the bed. He watched her
carefully, arrogance written all over his face as he
waited for her next question. She ignored the urge to
ask him who he was. She wouldn't give him the
satisfaction!

"Goodbye." She slipped her purse strap up to her
shoulder and reached for her bags, intending to
leave him in the room alone. But a viselike arm
clamped around her waist and pulled her back
against his hard-muscled body. Strangely enough,
she had been expecting it and didn't try to wrestle
out of his grip.

"Is this a game to you? I assure you that I don't
play by your rules. If you don't let me go it won't
bother me in the least to scream for the cleaning
woman. She's still there, you know." Her voice was
calm, her eyes staring straight ahead at the door.
Years of perfecting the art of hiding her emotions
came to her rescue.

His warm breath stirred the small strands of hair
that carelessly curled around her ear. The deep
rumble that passed for his laugh was more felt than
heard, vibrating against her back to send a definite

tremor through her body. Was this man dangerous? Was he insane?

"I'm afraid you don't understand," she placated him. "All I want you to do is to let me go. I'll discuss Mr. Cole with you in the lobby, where I met him. But not like this." She tried to sound cool and relaxed, not realizing that he could feel her rib cage freeze as she held her breath in anticipation of his answer.

"Reach your foot out and push both suitcases against the door," he demanded, his grip tightening ever so slightly.

She did as she was told, scooting each of them so close to the door that it couldn't be opened without knocking them out of the way.

He tugged lightly, pulling her even closer to him. Her heart stopped beating as his hand circled, then deliberately cupped, one firm breast encased in lacy nylon.

"For a girl who's hiring a stud, you're very nervous." He made his low opinion of her quite clear. "All I want to do is talk to you."

"Hiring implies that I have a choice in the man. You're giving me none." She tried to raise her arms, but his iron hold kept them glued to her sides. Her breath was coming quickly, as if she had run a mile. She was frightened and strove to control it. She forced herself to relax and he momentarily let down his guard in response. She quickly jerked one arm free and jabbed her elbow hard into his stomach. He gasped and immediately released his already light grip on her.

There was no time to wonder or worry. She

grabbed her purse and bags, then ran out of the door without looking back. It wasn't until she got into the elevator that she began to giggle. The giggle turned into a laugh and the laugh to salty tears.

Perhaps he had learned his lesson. Never trust a female animal when she's preparing a nest.

2

Anythin' wrong, little gal?" Sam's narrowed, knowing eyes saw more than most people realized. He knew with a protective, fatherly instinct that something was wrong with the girl he had in his own mind adopted as a daughter six years ago. He bit off a plug of his favorite chewing tobacco and patiently waited for her to answer.

"No," she answered absently, staring out of the pickup's window at the foothills of the mountains she loved so well. They surrounded Salt Lake City, making the plateau feel like a protected nest. "It was a productive trip." His face flashed through her mind's eye again. He was shorter than Brandon Cole by several inches. Perhaps he was two or three inches shy of six feet, but his bunched muscles proclaimed that he was in far better shape than most men would ever be. A chill shot down her spine as she recalled the hold he had used on her. He hadn't

34

wanted to hurt her, that much had been obvious. As a matter of fact, his grasp had been almost reluctant until he had reached for her breast. Her anger rose again at the thought. That was typical of the arrogant male!

"If I didn't know better, I'd say you were on the warpath about somethin'," Sam observed.

She reached over and patted the gnarled hand on the steering wheel, her eyes still focused on the mountains ahead. "Not really, Sam. I'm just tired and eager to get home." She gave him a rueful smile. "I guess I just don't travel well. I missed my own pillow."

The old cowboy muttered something inaudible under his breath before silencing himself for the rest of the short trip from Salt Lake City to Park City. He had made this trip often on business for The Loose Noose, and he knew the territory like the back of his hand. He also knew the woman sitting next to him. Although she had a temper that would rival the devil's, it took more than plenty to stir her emotions to the point they were at then. The funny thing was that she didn't even realize just how angry she was, and she wouldn't until someone said the wrong thing and she jumped down his throat faster than he could swallow.

"Jeff said he wanted to get you a load of wood before the summer was over so it could season a little. He didn't know if you wanted any for yourself or if he should just deliver it to the bar."

"Tell him I want two cords delivered to the bar. I'll take what I need from there. I'm not home enough to use much wood." She continued to stare out of the window, still seeing *his* face through the thick glass.

"Not last year, you weren't. But I thought the purpose of hiring so many workers this winter was so you wouldn't have to work so much," Sam persisted, hoping he'd push her enough so that she would blow her stack before they got to the bar. She was deadly when she was in a temper.

Still she continued to stare out of the window. "I'm not sure yet. I'll let you know as soon as I am." Why had his chin looked so stubborn? He should have aroused only her anger, but instead their meeting had been stimulating, a challenge. He had made her feel excited inside, where it didn't show.

Thirty minutes later Caro got out of the muddy pickup and climbed the freshly painted wooden steps of her quaint Victorian home. The house was painted a delft blue with crisp white shutters and cupolas. Lace curtains and potted plants created an old-fashioned feeling, but the house itself was full of the latest modern conveniences.

But for once she didn't notice with pride all that the house represented or what she had accomplished. Instead, she inserted her key in the lock and opened the door without once glancing in admiration at the oval-glassed door she had ordered from Europe because it was the perfect touch for her perfect home.

"Do you want a cold beer, Sam?" she called over her shoulder as she went down the hallway toward the kitchen, dropping her heavy shoulder bag on the small horsehair sofa along the wall as she went. "I'm having some tea."

"I have to get back to the bar. I'm opening at four-thirty today, remember?" Saturdays were so busy that they had begun to open early to take full advantage of the crowd's loose money. Beer, French fries, and cheeseburgers were the order of the day until seven-thirty, when the band began to play. Then came the mixed-drinks group, the sophisticates with their fashionable makeup and designer jeans.

"Did you get enough avocado dip from that new food broker?" Caro called, turning on the gas burner under the copper kettle.

"Yes, and the customers love it. The late-night ski crowd thought it was homemade." He followed her into the kitchen, his battered Stetson in his hand.

"Then you don't need me for anything tonight?"

"Not unless you want to sing with the band." His eyes twinkled. "I could always listen to your cater-waulin', you know that."

She grinned back, knowing that he loved to tease her almost as much as he loved to hear her sing. He was a one-man fan club, and Caro never lost the wonderful feeling that came with knowing that she was pleasing someone whenever she sang and Sam listened. —

His teasing look fled to be replaced by one of concern. "Did you talk to that attorney? Did he manage to talk you out of your crazy plan?"

"I'm going through with it, Sam." She turned off the whistling kettle, not quite willing to put her ideas into words. The facts seemed logical until she spoke them aloud.

"I just don't see you doing this, Caro," he began, only to have her interrupt him.

"I want a good, healthy baby with all the chances life can give him or her. Common sense tells me that in order for that to happen, heredity must be taken into account." They had been over this ground before, but she would explain to him for however long it took, because he was her mother, father, and best friend all rolled into one.

"I'll bet if you tried, someone would let you adopt a baby, even if you are single."

"Why should I adopt when I'm perfectly capable of having a child of my own?" She tried to reason with him but could see from the confused look in his eyes that she hadn't convinced him. "Besides, if I adopted I would always worry that someday someone could take the baby away from me, either because they had changed their mind or because I own a bar, which isn't the best occupation to be in when you're trying to attain respectability."

"But if you go through with this, some guy could come back and claim the baby anyway," he argued logically.

"Except that I would have the ammunition to argue with. I would have my baby plus a paper that the father had signed, giving up all rights. It would be nearly impossible for him to fight that kind of custody." Her voice was soft but determined, and she could see by the look in Sam's old gray eyes that he accepted her determination, even if he didn't understand it, even before he shook his head and walked toward the back door.

"I'll call you tomorrow and let you know the day's receipts." He spoke in a low monotone that told Caro he was going to pout for a while. A small, sad grin touched the corners of her mouth.

"Fine. See you Monday," she called as he shut the door and walked slowly around the drive to the front of the house and the old pickup plastered with bright green-and-yellow bumper stickers proclaiming "Be a loose goose at The Loose Noose." She grabbed a sturdy porcelain mug from the cupboard and reached for a tea bag. Damn! Why couldn't he see just how important this baby was to her? Look at all the luxuries she could give a child. *Her* child! Almost anyone would envy the wealth she had accumulated over the past years.

The string from the tea bag dangled down the side of her cup, swinging in gentle counterpoint to her steps as she walked into the front hall and toward the living-room window to watch Sam drive off. He was such a good friend; it seemed a shame to strain their friendship over a matter as deeply personal as this.

Her stiffened shoulder muscles, held tensely all day, suddenly loosened and slumped. She was exhausted. Whether she admitted it or not, for the past three days her nerves had been strung as tightly as nylon thread on a wooden spool. It wasn't easy to interview three candidates for the position of biological father. It wasn't easy at all.

Her legs quivered and Caro decided that it would be easier to slump on the furniture than against the wall. The couch's cushions were soft, and her head rested wearily on its high back. She closed her eyes and allowed her mind to wander, perhaps seeking the answer to the depression that had been weighing her down.

Born in a charity hospital in the Midwest and abandoned at the age of three to be raised in a series of foster homes, Caro had learned at an early age that if you weren't bound by blood, nothing would win you first place in someone's heart. That lesson had been reinforced many times over in the years that followed as she was shifted from one foster home to another. In most cases the slights hadn't been anything that she could put a finger on, just a feeling that if push came to shove, she, as the outsider, would be shoved. If something went wrong it was usually for the one who didn't belong, not for the one who had always been there.

As Caro had entered her early teens she had become more introspective, a loner in a complex system of loners. But in that loneliness a resiliency had been born that would help her achieve that which she wanted with all her heart: to succeed in life according to everyone else's measure. She wanted wealth and success so she could say, "See, I did it! I made a success of myself when everyone said I wasn't winner material!" But most of all, she wanted roots.

Caro was singing in local bands by the time she was sixteen and traveling all over the country by the time she was a year older. She had taken odd jobs during the day as a waitress, dishwasher, or janitor—anything that paid enough to live on and where her employer wasn't worried about how long she would be in town. At night she would sing; the noise and collective energy kept her awake and on her feet until the gig was over. Then it would be time to collapse in her sleeping bag on the floor of one of the guy's rooms or backstage at the club where they were playing. The next morning the cycle would begin all over again.

Eight years later her current band was playing Salt Lake City at the same time that Caro discovered that she finally had enough for a small down payment on a business. Which business she was going to invest in, she didn't know. At that time she hadn't even cared, so heady was the secret knowledge that she could finally be her own boss, earn money, start to grow the deep roots she had always envied others.

It was that same night, in a country and western dance hall on the edge of Salt Lake City, that Caro met Sam. She had wandered into the wide back alley for a breath of fresh air between sets when the stage door opened and three men walked out, all three of them drunk with liquor and good times.

One stopped to ogle and then violate her privacy with his words. "Honey, you're one fine piece of—"

His words were cut off by a moving shadow in the darkness. "That's enough, Hank. Shut your mouth before you're in real trouble."

Within moments the men were gone and the shadow turned into substance . . . the bouncer from the bar, who had decided to take a cigarette break. He had been there all along.

She lowered her defenses to thank him, then left them down. There was a mental kinship between them from the very moment of their meeting. From that time on Sam watched over her like an older brother, making sure that none of the customers got too close without her permission. She, in turn, talked to him of her dreams, her work, her hopes in life. He listened without saying much, content just with being a sounding board.

By the time the band's two weeks at the club were over, Caro and Sam had become fast friends, soul mates. He knew about her background and she knew something about his. She knew that he had been married to a woman who loved him more than he loved her. Then she had died and he had realized too late just how much he had taken for granted. She knew that his misspent youth had superstitioned him into believing that he had to atone for his sins, and she also knew that he was lonely. He honestly believed that his loneliness was a punishment. She knew that he treated her as if she were his daughter, watching over her with the protectiveness that she supposed all daughters wished that their fathers felt. It seemed almost crazy, but it seemed right, too.

On the last day the band was to play at that bar, Sam came in and quietly stood at the back of the room during rehearsal. When the rehearsal was over and Caro stepped down from the stage, Sam motioned to her.

"I found something I thought might interest you," he whispered in his gravelly voice, handing her an ad torn from a local newspaper.

She scanned it quickly, then reread it slowly. "Where is Park City?"

"In the heart of the Utah skiing country, about thirty minutes from here. I'll take you."

Within two weeks Caro had signed the papers that made her the lessee of a building in downtown Park City. If, within a year, she decided to buy said building her payments would be put toward that goal. Sam would be the manager of her newly acquired dance hall, The Loose Noose.

With the benefit of the knowledge that Sam had stored up during his years as a bouncer and Caro's clear, crisp, innovative mind, the place had bloomed into an overnight success. No one saw the careful planning, the worrying, the detailed paperwork that had gone into the project. To the casual observer it just looked like luck.

Six years later Caro offered Sam a partnership, which he predictably declined. He worked for a salary and a percentage of the profits, and that was all he said he wanted. With the exception of his fatherly relationship with Caro, he was still a loner.

The previous year Caro had built her dream house, a large, Victorian-style home that looked as if it had perched in the foothills since the mining heyday that was Park City's claim to fame. Its completion had been a highlight in Caro's life; the house became the symbol of everything she had ever wanted to attain. Like the trophy it was, it stood for respectability and stability, roots and beauty, and success.

She sighed, leaning forward to place her mug on the coffee table before leaning back once more.

The house, although it provided everything material that she had ever wanted, still hadn't been the cure for that small, empty ache somewhere deep down inside her. That ache would only be filled by having people to love, a family. Even though Sam gave her his love, it wasn't enough. She wanted her own flesh and blood. She wanted a child.

Thus had begun the soul-searching and the end result: the search for a father.

She didn't hear the car door slam because her mind was still wandering through memories. When the doorbell rang she jumped, startled.

The opaque beveled glass gave only a hazy clue to the identity of the person on the other side. It was a man, not too tall and broad shouldered. He stood immobile, a dark silhouette against the late afternoon sun.

She opened the door, then froze when she saw her visitor. "You!"

His smile was cold, his eyes narrowed as he sized up her reaction. He was apparently satisfied that she was surprised.

"I'd love to come in, thank you." He took a step forward and walked over the threshold, knowing that she wouldn't block his way. Electricity filled the air, almost literally crackling as the emotional sparks flew between them. Caro stood back in an attempt to escape the aura that surrounded him.

"How did you find me?" Somehow she already knew. She had known on the way home, although she hadn't wanted to admit it.

"I followed you." He continued to stand in the middle of the long hallway, patiently waiting for her next question.

"Why?"

"I think that's obvious. I need to talk to you. I want to discuss Brandon Cole."

"I won't discuss him unless he's here." She knew that she could have said anything and it would have made no difference. The end result would be the same. They would talk.

"Should we discuss this over a cup of coffee, a glass of wine, or just sit across from one another in your living room?"

She gave a heavy sigh. "Whatever."

"The living room," he decided quickly, then walked in slowly, admiring the decor before sitting down in the ecru and forest green wingback chair. "Very nice." He acted as if his presence there was nothing out of the ordinary.

"Thank you." She sat on the couch across from him.

"I talked to your lawyer and I spoke with Brandon, and we all agree that he won't do for your purpose." He hesitated over the last word, a knowing gleam in his chocolate-brown eyes.

"Did my attorney tell you just how long I've been looking for someone who can qualify?" Her voice was calm and deliberate, but she was seething inside. Her tensed nerves were wound up like a mechanical toy, until she thought her spring would pop. It didn't matter that she hadn't been too thrilled with the idea of Brandon Cole as a donor either. Now she would defend her position to the death.

He nodded. "Yes."

"Mr. Cole seems to need the money."

"He always needs money that he doesn't have to

work for." His tone was cruel, cold. "And that's why he won't earn it this way. By the time this was over he'd have no self-respect left and the girl who really loves him would be gone from him forever. He'd lose everything."

"Except eight thousand dollars." Caro spoke dryly, ignoring the pulse pounding in the hollow of her throat.

"To quote an old saying, 'Money isn't everything.'" His eyes glinted once more. "Besides, he doesn't know half as much about you as you know about him. He wants to know a few things, too." His eyes continued to rove insolently up and down her figure before he finally stared into her eyes as if he could read what she was thinking.

"All he had to do was ask. He couldn't have been too concerned; his first and last questions were about money."

He shrugged, intimating that it was inconsequential to him. "Well, I have a few that aren't." She nodded and waited for the interrogation to begin. She wasn't disappointed.

"How old are you?"

"Thirty-five."

"Ever been married?"

"Never."

"Affairs, now or ever?"

"It's none of your business."

One brow rose in obvious disbelief and he quickly moved on to the next question. "Boyfriends?"

"On occasion, but not at present."

"Why not choose a boyfriend for this? You're

good-looking enough to entice a man into bed without telling him why." It was the most backhanded compliment that Caro had ever heard!

"I thought of that until a man I was dating told me that his ex-wife had had a child born with crippling arthritis. It suddenly dawned on me that you never know what's in the genetic background of a boyfriend. Shortly after that there was a case in the paper where a man found out that his old girlfriend had given birth to a baby boy a few years earlier. He sued for custody and won. I thought those two issues were important, so I contacted a lawyer and decided to eliminate any forseeable problems."

"You have covered most bases, haven't you?" he muttered absently.

"Of course. I'm trying to protect my child."

"But most of all you're protecting yourself." His sparkling dark eyes strained to see into her mind. Suddenly he leaned back, a small smile flitting across his craggy face. For one crazy moment she had the feeling that he knew exactly what she was feeling. The fight she was having with herself against his magnetism must have been apparent. He knew it and he liked it. "You want a child so badly that you would consider hiring someone for the job?" he reiterated.

"Correction. I *will* hire someone for the job," she said with more bravado than she felt. She wished she could concentrate on his words as deeply as she was paying attention to the movement of his full mouth. She was more attracted to this man than she had been to any man in years. She cursed silently. Why had the fates seen fit to send someone to upset her equilibrium? Hadn't she been doing fine by herself all these years?

His eyes dropped to her hands as they rested in her lap. They gave away the nervousness she felt. He glanced back up. "Then hire me," he said calmly, letting his words float gently down like feathers before they hit her like sledgehammers.

Her face went blank. "No."

He leaned forward. "Why not?"

"I don't know you or anything about you."

"I can give you any information you need to know."

"No."

"Why?" He smiled. "Afraid?"

"Of course not! I just don't see what this whole situation has to do with you." Her eyes probed his, her forehead creasing.

He leaned back. "I happen to think that I'm more suited to the job. My medical information is being processed into letter form now to be given to you if you accept me as a substitute."

"Are you that opposed to my choosing Brandon Cole?"

"Yes." He clamped his mouth shut, apparently unwilling to speak further of that young man.

Did he know something about Brandon Cole that she didn't? Had Brandon lied about his credentials? "Why you?"

"Because I'm available and I fit the requirements and you, obviously, are not going to drop this scheme. Better me than someone else."

"Is Brandon Cole someone special to you?"

"I know his parents very well, and they would be terribly hurt by his actions." His eyes narrowed. He stared up at a bright splash of color in the large painting on the wall above her head. His mind had obviously been diverted to another thought. Then he looked back at her again. "I'm perfect for the job and I can prove it."

"How?"

"Give me an hour to have my family physician call your physician and confirm my background. He's known me since I was three years old and has my records starting from when I was born."

"No."

He ran a hand around the back of his neck in exasperation. "Now why not?"

"It's none of your business." Her mind flew in a thousand different directions. She couldn't seem to get a single thought in order.

"I have everything you require and more." His tone was dry. He knew that she was having trouble stringing her thoughts together in some semblance of order.

"It doesn't matter."

"Why not? I'm not as tall as Brandon, but my height's average." He grinned disarmingly. "I used to be better looking than I am now. Perhaps not as good-looking as Brandon, but not bad. And I boxed in college, while he never went at all." He certainly wasn't ashamed of his looks, and Caro could understand why. He wasn't the pretty-boy type. He was a man with a capital M; Caro could almost see the sex appeal oozing from his pores. He was extremely potent and he knew it. "I could show you baby pictures of me and my bare bottom on a fur rug," he suggested with the hint of a teasing smile.

"You don't even know if you can have children." Her voice cracked. Why was she bothering to continue this silly conversation? She knew why. Because he was too fascinating to be ignored. Because he was hypnotizing her with his southern drawl.

"I have all the proper equipment." He dryly stated the obvious. "A test can prove the rest." He nodded in mock deference. "As for a character reference, I've known Mike Avery since we were ten. He grew up one block from my parents' home. We've been the best of friends and I'm sure you'll find that he'll swear to my good conduct and sense of fair play in business."

"But . . ." Her thoughts were still scrambled, her mind whirling.

"And make no mistake, Brandon has withdrawn," he emphasized. "So, unless you wish to continue your search, which your attorney doesn't think is wise, you'll have to settle for me."

"I can't."

"Why?"

"We aren't compatible." She grabbed frantically at a straw.

"We don't have to be. If I'm willing to do this, I don't see why you shouldn't be. After all, I'm giving up my child; you're just investing money." He didn't wait to hear her answer. "What was the original plan?"

"When the right time came, my physician would

handle the rest." Her face was white with strain, but her eyes were clear as they stared at him.

"I see." He stared thoughtfully somewhere above her head as he again rubbed the back of his neck. Suddenly he looked back at her, surprising her with his intentness. "I'm going to leave you for an hour or so. Then I'll return, and whatever your answer is, I'll accept it." He stood, his broad frame almost dwarfing the chair behind him. "But mark my words, you don't have much choice in the matter. Brandon is out of the question." He smiled, confident of what her decision would be. "And be here, or else I'll have to assume that you want me to wait around indefinitely."

She stood also, her face blank. "I'll do as I damn well please, Mr. . . . ?"

"J.T. It stands for Joseph Thomas," he filled in with a grin.

"Mr. Thomas," she said, ignoring his first name.

He seemed about to say something, then shrugged and walked to the door with lithe grace. "I'll see you in an hour or so." His voice was mockingly polite.

The door shut quietly and Caro stood where she was, able to watch him walk down the front walk to his car, a red Porsche. The engine roared into action and then the sound dwindled away in the summer air as he drove off. Caro slowly sat down but continued to stare sightlessly out the window.

She had had doubts concerning her plan before, but she'd always been able to talk herself back into the rightness of it. But now . . . now she was more confused than ever. Not because she had changed her mind about the baby, but because she knew the baby's prospective father! She blinked her eyes. What was she thinking of! Could she be seriously considering his crazy, half-baked proposal? Yes, a small voice laughed at her. He's handsome and challenging and intelligent and . . . willing. What did the difference in the candidate make as long as the outcome was the same? She wanted a baby and he was willing to provide her with one. So what if she suspected that he wanted to cheat Brandon Cole out of the money? That wasn't her problem. Besides, if Brandon Cole had wanted the job enough, he would have given her more encouragement. As it was, Caro had a feeling that he had only been going through the motions for reasons of his own, but that he hadn't really wanted to go through with it unless she pressed him.

Chocolate brown eyes with a golden twinkle danced in front of her and that, she knew, was the problem. Joseph Thomas was oozing with sex appeal, and she was physically drawn to him when that was the last thing she wanted to feel toward any man. Her life had been free of men and the emotional entanglements they represented for years, and she wanted it to stay that way. She wanted to stay free to lead her own life and not subjugate herself to someone else's wants and needs. And she wanted to take a totally clinical view of the man she chose to be the father of her child, but she was unable to manage that with Joseph. His masculinity got in the way.

Suddenly she realized just how ridiculous her stand was. Wouldn't that very masculinity be a desirable characteristic if her child were a boy? Didn't most women seek out that very quality in a mate? Although this would be a temporary relationship at best, wasn't it still just as important? Suddenly she laughed, a bright sound that echoed through the room.

Of course she would accept his offer. It could prove to be an asset that he knew her and knew where she lived, because he would also know that she could care for a child. As long as he was willing to submit to the tests and sign the papers, she would be a fool to turn down his offer!

With that she stood and reached for her cup, then walked to the kitchen with a jaunty step.

After further discussing the issue with herself for almost an hour, the problem was solved. Mr. Joseph Thomas would be the father of her child.

She notified her physician concerning Mr. Thomas's credentials, only to find that his doctor had already forwarded the information and everything had been approved wholeheartedly by everyone concerned. Her doctor, who had originally doubted her ability to find a man for such a job, pronounced her a magician. He was still worried about her own peace of mind in years to come, hoping that the guilt of buying a parent wouldn't do her harm later, but Mr. Thomas's physician had apparently helped to persuade him that this was probably the only willing candidate in the state of Utah.

She had contacted her attorney, Mike Avery, and confirmed what Mr. Thomas had said. Mike's blessing of J.T. was nearly wholehearted, but his voice had held a hint of caution and a thread of warning. He had also asked to be released from interviewing any more applicants. He didn't believe there was another man in Utah who would fit the bill and abide by the rules. After his warning that she was playing with danger, Caro had hung up, realizing that it was probably this man . . . or no man. So much for all her worries, she thought dryly.

When Mr. Thomas—she couldn't think of him as J.T.—showed up on her doorstep exactly on time, she smiled. Another plus for the candidate. A small bunch of lavender wrapped in florists' paper was handed to her as a peace offering, and the smile on his face said that he knew just how much thinking she had had to do and that he hoped he could sway her.

They sat and quietly discussed the terms of the agreement Mike had drawn up, with Joseph Thomas agreeing to almost everything.

Suddenly Caro felt elated. She didn't know if it was because she had made her decision or because she was closer to her goal of having a child of her own than she had been before, but her emotions soared.

She wanted him to be the father of her child as much as he wanted that to happen, too.

"No artificial insemination. That's final. I agree with everything except that. I happen to believe that a good beginning is one of the most important provisions I can make for our offspring. Also, I'll stay with you until your conception is a fact."

"You're crazy," she muttered under her breath,

her eyes wide as she watched him relax as if he had been built for her chair. Her forehead was dotted with perspiration, while he looked as cool as an evening breeze.

He stood. "Are you embarrassed to make love with someone? To conceive a child in the manner that nature devised? It seems the most normal way to begin a baby."

"I don't want to discuss this," she snapped, her hand slicing the air like a knife. "I'll decide how my child will be conceived."

"Our child," he mumbled almost absently as he stared out the front window. "And if you think you're likely to get another candidate soon, you'd better call your lawyer and reconfirm with him. I'm sure he's smart enough to tell you just how slim your chances are, especially in Utah, where religion and the family are revered above everything."

"I don't believe this," she continued to mutter, no longer angry at him as much as remembering her own physician's words on that same subject. Knowing he was right didn't make this problem any easier to solve. Why did he have to be so damn stubborn!

"You either buy those rules or you can forget about the baby. You've already decided that I'm your best candidate or you wouldn't have agreed at all. I'm only taking it one step further," he reasoned. "Now, which will it be, the normal way or not at all?"

"Nothing can be done until the proper procedures are followed. You must go through the same tests and exams that Brandon Cole did," she bluffed, playing for time in which her chaotic mind could wrestle with the problem. Right then she couldn't think of a thing to say against his reasoning. "If you can't . . ." She let the sentence trail off, giving him room to withdraw.

"My doctor's already taken care of most of that, but I'll have the rest taken care of tomorrow," he verified. "Now, what other arguments do you have?"

She found herself following the line of his gaze to stare out the window. Was this the result of a bizarre idea that should have been shelved, as Sam had said? She glanced up at him, knowing that she felt an invisible pull toward this man and also realizing just how much that feeling frightened her. It had been years since she had felt any emotion toward a man. She had thought that part of her was dead, buried in the business of everyday living. Was he right? Despite all the care she had given to finding the right man, was she overlooking the fact that children should be conceived in, if not love, perhaps liking? Once more she was becoming confused, her mind whirling—too much was happening at one time. She would have to go by instinct, something she never did. Sam always said she was too controlled, that she kept too tight a rein on her emotions. Perhaps he was right.

Her mouth made up her mind for her. "I choose the time and place?" She was amazed at herself. Never in a million years would she have believed that she would go along with him! Yet there she was, agreeing as if it were someone else's business she was arranging. But in the back of her mind was the reassuring idea that she could back out of his crazy version of her plan at any time.

"You choose the time and place." He grinned disarmingly, his charm turned toward her full force, stunning her with its impact.

"It's a deal," she said, holding out her hand to be clasped by his.

"Good. Now, where do you want me to sleep?" At her open-mouthed stare, a twinkle invaded his eyes. "In the guest room, I'd wager. Which is fine. We need to get to know each other a little better before we proceed any further."

There was a fated air surrounding the entire episode. For some reason, nothing that had happened was really a shock to her. She had unconsciously known that they would see each other again ever since she first stared at him in the restaurant. She had become positive when he rescued her earring. During the drive home she had known that he was following. Even when he walked into her home to say such wild things, he had actually made some crazy sort of sense to her.

Within an hour he was established in the guest bedroom. Two hours later they were eating dinner together in the kitchen. Three hours later they had cleaned the kitchen and were sitting at the table playing gin rummy.

And four hours later they were both tucked into separate beds, Caro staring at the ceiling of the dark room. What in heaven's name did they think they were doing? she mused. This was a matter of a child's life and she was worried about whether or not he found her attractive! She pounded her pillow and tried to concentrate on a mental picture of the last page of The Loose Noose ledger.

Anything was better than admitting to herself what happened to her nervous system every time she imagined being captured in his arms.

3

Caro spread her cards on the table. "Gin," she crowed, her eyes lighting up with mischievous laughter as she watched J.T.'s obvious irritation. He was a natural winner, and to lose, especially to a female, was just not his idea of a good time.

"You're not a professional gambler, are you?" he asked, his eyes softening in admiration as he watched her face fill with unabashed enjoyment.

"Nope," she answered. "But I *am* good!"

J.T. gathered up the scattered cards and began shuffling. His fingers were long and slender, with a sensitivity all their own. They caught her eye and she couldn't help staring. Her vibrant imagination ran riot on seeing those supple hands move and bend in a natural rhythm.

"I've spent two days with you now and you still haven't explained to me why you hate men." His voice was easy, his tone conversational. He was attempting to put her at ease while getting the answers to questions for which he definitely wanted answers.

She gave her best business smile. "Nothing personal," she retorted lightly. "Your sex just doesn't have a lot to recommend it, that's all."

"And feeling that way, you still want to place yourself in a position where you have a fifty-fifty chance of giving birth to a son?"

"It's not the same."

"No matter how cute it is, a wolf cub grows into a wolf."

"Don't patronize me, Joseph. I know what I'm doing. What I don't know is why *you're* here," she snapped. "It can't be for the money. You're already making a good salary, if your clothing is anything to go by."

"J.T.," he corrected automatically. "And don't get off the subject, Caro. Do you think that just because you raise that male child he'll be so different from the rest of his sex? And if he is, will he ever be able to find happiness? After all, he won't fit in with his male contemporaries if you have your way."

Her eyes flashed silver in anger as Caro took a deep breath. "If you're trying to confuse me, you'll have to try harder. I don't need your heckling any more than I need you."

"Don't be so defensive; you give yourself away." He grinned. "You need me, all right."

"No, your kind are all over, ready at the first opportunity to take whatever they can get." She felt breathless, invigorated. Arguing with him was a challenge.

His eyes bored into her, forcing her to admit to the

real feelings she had hidden deep inside, allowing them to reach the surface.

His voice was low, soft, but threaded with the strength of steel. "I'm one of a kind and you know it, or I wouldn't still be here."

"I hate you." It came unbidden.

"Good." His voice was now laced with satisfaction. "That's the first honest emotion you've shown. Now, perhaps we can get on with this relationship." His dark eyes twinkled in derisive amusement. "Lady, we're gonna make one hell of a baby!" He gave a heartbreaking smile. Just before turning to leave the room, he perused her slim body all the way down to her toes and back up to her golden blond hair. Then he winked audaciously.

She fumed, but he was right. They *would* make one perfect child.

"Are you coming by the club tonight? I want to go over a few figures with you," Sam grumbled into the telephone, making sure that his chewing tobacco was out of the way so Caro could understand him.

"I'll be there around ten. See you then." She hung up, quickly doing calculations in her head to figure the total of three nights' receipts. Of course, the bills for beer and food would take about fifty percent of that total.

Her hand still rested on the phone, her thoughts focused somewhere inside.

"Are you through, or should I wait and make my calls in the morning?" Joseph's voice rumbled from behind her, sending an instant, light chill of awareness down her spine.

"Be my guest." Mockery laced her voice, her glacial eyes expressing her feelings far better than words ever could.

He didn't move toward the phone; instead he continued to stare at her. She looked as if she were poised for flight. "Are we going out tonight?"

"Not we, *me.*"

"And what makes you think I'll stay here by myself?"

"If you want to continue this 'relationship,' then you'll do as you're told."

His eyes twinkled at her blatant challenge. "Just because you're older than I am, it doesn't mean you can boss me around."

Her face whitened. With everything else going topsy-turvy this week, including her feelings for this confidently arrogant man, she had never asked him his age!

"How much older?" Her voice was strained.

"Does it matter?" Once more he held the trump card.

"Does it matter? Of course it matters! How old are you?" Her hands were clenched behind her.

"Older than my youngest brother," he quipped, then took mercy on her. "Behave yourself and I might tell you . . . later." He turned and walked toward the kitchen, apparently no longer interested in making his phone calls. Caro watched him stroll down the hall in his tight jeans and expensive striped jersey, her hands still clenched behind her. She cursed solidly under her breath.

Forcing herself to assume a semblance of calm, Caro followed him to the back of the house and watched as he put the kettle on to boil, all the while whistling a popular country and western tune slightly off key. Strangely enough, it wasn't anger that she felt toward him, this stranger who had come into her life just days ago. It was frustration.

She had been in charge of her life ever since leaving her last foster home. She had made decisions that most men never had the opportunity to make, both in her personal life and in the business world. She had founded a business that demanded expertise, foresight, and a keen mind. She had fought the odds that came because she was a woman, and she had won. She had done all that—until three days ago when Joseph had showed up on her doorstep and she had begun to act like a star-struck, naive teenager. But now it was time to get control of herself and her situation.

"I'm sorry I was rude, Joseph. For some reason we don't seem to be compatible. I think it might be better for both of us if we call this arrangement off." Did her voice sound composed enough? She hoped so.

"I accept your apology." He glanced over his shoulder as he reached for a cup from the shelf. "But as we businessmen say, the rest is garbage."

"So the big man said to put the little woman in her place." Her voice dripped with fury.

Joseph's eyes lingered on the impatient thrust of her breasts, the smallness of her waist, the slight rounding of her hips. He made visual love to her, stroking her with his soft velvet looks before his glance locked with hers to make sure she understood exactly what he wanted.

"Are you so small-minded that you can only see a woman playing one role in one place?" he asked. "Why can't a woman be at home in the kitchen and in the boardroom? Can't she be both under me and above me?"

"Not this woman. This woman wants you to get out of her house. This woman admits that she can't cope with your kind of man and prefers to continue searching for her child's prospective father somewhere else." Her voice shook with emotion. She had never before felt such a strong attraction to anyone as she did to him. She was completely confused and upset. All she really wanted was to regain control of her own world, no matter how small it was.

Her words were like lead cannonballs bouncing off the wooden floor. And when they stopped, the silence echoed so loudly through the room that she could hear herself breathe.

Joseph turned fully around, his back straight. His hands were loose at his sides, but the almost golden light in his eyes proved that he wasn't as relaxed as he looked. He continued to stare until she couldn't look at him any longer. The silence went on and on and on. The hall clock ticked; a horn honked in the distance. Still neither of them moved.

"Your doctor told mine that your fertile time is in a week or so. Is he right?"

Caro's heart stopped beating, but his rich drawl continued. "You can't find anyone to take my place and, after the past four days, you can't really find anything wrong with me, so you lose by default. I'm staying."

"Why?" Her voice was barely a whisper.

His look conveyed his low opinion of her intelligence. "Because I have no bad habits, I've got the right genes, and I'm available." He walked around the kitchen table and stood directly in front of her, his head barely four or five inches above hers but his massive shoulders blocking the rest of the kitchen from her view. "And the reason you're afraid isn't because I might harm you, but because you might allow your emotions more freedom than they've ever had." He took a deep breath, his eyes pinning her to the spot. "And, lady, that scares the hell out of you."

She could hardly breathe; her eyes were caught by his full mouth as it moved to form the words she didn't want to hear but couldn't ignore. "You're insane." She spoke more to herself than to him, but he didn't realize that.

His arms slid around her waist, bringing the lower part of his body into direct contact with her slimmer form. "No, I'm not, and you know it." She watched with fascination as his lips came down to possess hers and unconsciously formed her mouth to the mold of his desire.

His touch was everything she had feared. His fingers firmly traced the trail of her backbone as it smoothly indented at her waist, while his other hand held her close to feel his beginning need of her. His tongue traveled slowly through the crevices of her mouth, seeking to meld with hers. His firm lips moved slowly across hers, asking and receiving a response she couldn't withhold. He pressured her with a hand here, fingers there, his breath warm upon her cheek. He forced her to react to him until she was dizzy with a slow, seeping lethargy that wound its way through her body to wipe out all other feelings. Her legs were suddenly rubbery. She twined her arms around his neck for support and to feel the muscles and sinews of his body, bringing her breasts into intimate, electric contact with the hardness of his broad chest. She instinctively sought to fulfill her newfound hunger. Her heart constricted; her breathing became shallower than before. When his mouth left hers to seek the soft contours of her neck she arched compliantly to allow him access, unable to break the exquisite contact of skin against skin.

His touch was all that it could be and more. His skin was warm and tightly textured beneath her wandering hands. His lips moved to seek the corner of her mouth, then her cheek and neck, a wistful sigh escaping from his mouth as he sought the contours of her face. He was heaven and hell rolled into one, and if she had had more sense she would have been frightened by her own responses to him.

Once more his mouth foraged her own, and she tilted her head to give him easier admittance. At this moment his world was her world and she celebrated it.

The tea kettle suddenly sang out with a jarring sound and sanity slowly returned. Caro slipped out of J.T.'s arms and took two steps back, her breath still caught in her throat as she retreated both physically and emotionally from his overwhelming presence. His hands fell to his sides; he was relaxed, assured of the power of his persuasiveness by watching the vulnerable expression that crossed her face.

He turned off the burner and poured the water into the waiting teapot. He set two cups on the table before he sat down, leaving her to take a seat on the opposite side. She did, slowly, her legs still not strong enough to support her without the aid of a wall or a chair.

He broke the awkward silence with velvet words. "We're going to be very good together."

Her throat was dry, her mind confused with the myriad emotions that warred with her sanity. "It doesn't matter. We're not doing this for fun."

He gave a laugh. "Don't believe it. If making love wasn't designed to be one of the greatest feelings in the world, there would be no children and the human race would have been dead almost before it began."

She sipped her tea and pretended that she always kissed a man passionately, then sat down at the table to discuss sexual facts and fallacies.

"I disagree." Her skepticism was as apparent as his humor at the situation.

"And you know so much about it," he taunted, one slashing dark brow lifted in mockery.

"No, but I'm doing it, and my reasons have nothing to do with great feelings or emotions," she lied. She had to do so in order to gain control of her tumbling emotions. He seemed to make her react to him no matter what he said.

He grinned. "The nesting urge," he confirmed.

"You don't think women throughout history would have had more than one child if it weren't such a great experience getting pregnant, do you?"

"I'm afraid I'll have to allow you to answer that." Her voice sounded prim, but she couldn't help it. "You're the only one with that kind of experience."

"Not for long, Caro." His eyes darkened as his gaze pinned her to the chair. "Not for long."

A lump formed in her throat. "Am I some sort of a challenge to you? Is that what this is all about?"

The small, intimate smile he had worn was gone. A muscle knotted in the side of his jaw and he stood and rinsed his cup with a minimum of movement. "Yes."

She put her cup down and stared into the tea leaves that clung to the sides. She wished she hadn't asked that question.

The stomping of the dancers' booted feet could be heard all the way to the parking lot as the music blared through the room, overcoming the shouts of the patrons of The Loose Noose.

Caro hunched over the battered wooden Army surplus desk, her fingers flying over the adding machine as she whizzed through the columns of numbers on the ledger sheet in front of her. Sam sat across from her, his chair tilted back on two legs so that his dusty boots could rest on the front of the desk. His arms were folded behind his head as he stared at the corner of the room, completely relaxed.

Joseph sat on the worn leather couch against the wall and watched Caro from beneath lowered lids. The noise was muted in the office, although an occasional exuberant yell could still be heard, but Caro let nothing distract her. A few minutes later she leaned back, her smile telling Sam just how satisfied she was. "Your figures are right to the penny. And it's a pretty good take for the summertime."

He nodded. There was nothing for him to say; the ledger said it all.

She pushed a button under the desk top, still smiling. "What'll you have, Joseph?"

"J.T.," he reminded her again. "I'll have a beer, ma'am. What else would you drink in a place like The Loose Noose?" He grinned back. Her satisfaction was catching.

Sam finally let his feet drop to the floor with a thump as his chair came down on all four legs. "Hank's ready to go ahead with the building up in Snowhawk. The foundation's all laid. He's waiting for you to say the word and the walls will be next."

Caro's eyes grew distant, flicking to Joseph with an unspoken message for Sam.

Sam shrugged. He wasn't sure he understood what she was doing here with the man, but it was pretty obvious what he was interested in. It didn't really worry Sam, though. Caro was a big girl, and if she found someone to shoot sparks off of, then so be it. It was certainly better than that harebrained scheme she had been considering. This guy was definitely interested in her as a woman, and she was just as interested in him, if her occasional unguarded looks were anything to go by.

J.T. leaned back, watching the silent conversation between the two old friends. A waiter stuck his head in the door in response to the buzzer Caro had pushed earlier, and left a moment later with their order for drinks.

Finally J.T. spoke. "Did Caro explain the part I'm supposed to play in her life, Sam?"

The older man looked surprised, immediately sensing that a battle was about to begin.

"No, I didn't." Caro took up the conversational ball. "Did you expect me to?" She tossed her hair back, unconsciously throwing down the gauntlet in challenge.

His smile was almost feral. "I'm the hired hand, the stud who's supposed to father Caro's baby—a new toy she's decided she needs. Didn't you know?"

Disapproval was stamped all over Sam's face as he glanced from Joseph to Caro. "Is that who he is? That guy you interviewed in Salt Lake City?"

"No, Sam. Joseph is taking that guy's place." Caro spoke through gritted teeth, angry at being forced to explain Joseph's presence when she shouldn't have had to.

"I thought you were going to keep your home and occupation a secret? I thought this was goin' to be a case of the less known the better?" Sam asked, angry concern evident in his voice.

"It was—until I came on the scene," Joseph intervened. "And call me J.T., Sam. Only my mother calls me Joseph." He grinned at Caro, innocence written all over his rugged face. "But I had to change the rules of her game to suit myself. She's lucky. I might have been unscrupulous."

Sam walked over to the man on the couch and stared down at him as if trying to see something

others couldn't. He continued to stare even when the
bartender entered and set the tray of drinks down on
the desk before quickly departing.

Sam finally walked away and picked up his shot
glass of whiskey. He threw another glance over his
shoulder, unaware that Caro was holding her breath
in expectation. She realized that she was secretly
waiting to hear Sam's judgement of Joseph, because
she knew that that was exactly what he was going to
give her.

Sam's pale gray eyes stared at J.T. for a moment
before he spoke. "Caro is my boss and my friend. I
take care of my friends and make sure they don't get
hurt. If you hurt her more than this crazy, half-baked
scheme would have anyway, then keep a watch over
your shoulder, 'cause I'll be on the lookout for you."

J.T. grinned, not at all shaken. "And what if you
and I become friends, and *she* hurts *me?*"

Sam gave a rumbling laugh; he liked J.T. "You
two are going to give each other a run for the
money." His respect for J.T. was obvious and Caro's
eyes narrowed angrily; Sam's defection had shocked
her. As for J.T., he was relaxed and at ease, lounging
comfortably on the old leather couch. If only he
didn't have all that sex appeal that claimed her
attention whenever she got within seeing distance of
him.

"Don't humor him, Sam. He's already got the
biggest ego in Utah."

Both men chuckled. The old cowboy downed his
drink in one swallow and put down the glass with a
ritual thud before walking out of the office. "I'm

leaving you two alone. Don't call me unless one of you draws blood," he called from the doorway, and his shoulders moved with a laugh. "It oughta be some fight."

"A sensible man, that Sam," Joseph said complacently, leaning back on the sofa again, completely relaxed as a look of self-satisfaction crossed his face.

"He likes you. I don't know why, but he likes you," Caro said grudgingly. She was jealous. Sam had always been her friend, her family, her special and very private rock to lean on. It wasn't fair.

One dark brow rose in question. "I feel as if I should apologize, but I won't. He realizes just how insane your quest for a child is, the same as I do. But we're both willing to indulge your whims."

A chill went down Caro's spine. "And then you'll leave, never to return." She waited for him to repeat the promise, to comment, to laugh, to say something. Instead, he reached over and grabbed his bottle of beer, ignoring the chilled mug that sat beside it. "Won't you?" she finally questioned.

The lines deepened around his mouth. "Are you frightened, Caro? Good. It'll keep your mind busy enough so that you won't worry about the nights that are coming up."

"As far as I'm concerned, there are no nights coming."

J.T.'s voice turned hard and heavy, filled with promise. "Make no mistake, Caro. Either you and I march to your attorney's office, where you sign a piece of paper stating you won't pursue this crazy scheme any further, or I'm your man. There's no other option open to you." He leaned toward her. "Understand?"

"There's no way that you can hurt me, Joseph. And it's you who needs to march into that office. If you really expect to fill Brandon's shoes, you'd better sign the contracts. Is that understood?" Anger seared through her like a hot branding iron, almost blinding her with its heat.

"I've already signed the damn things, but don't think for a moment that I wouldn't turn this wonderful little tidbit of interesting information over to someone who could use it—*if* you crossed me. Your business would drop with a heavy thud. Just behave yourself, so I don't have to bother using a good contact who owes me a favor."

She stood, shaking with reaction. "Go to hell, Joseph Thomas. If it hurts my business, it will hurt yours, too." Suddenly she realized that she didn't even know where he lived, how to reach him, anything! Her dismay must have shown, because he grinned like a Cheshire cat before taking a swig from his beer bottle. "I'll do as I damn please."

"And by the way," he said as she stalked out the door, "I own an accounting firm. My clients would prefer to think the worst of me. I might be crooked enough to give them a better deal with the IRS." His words stopped her as she reached for the doorknob. "So fire away, pretty lady. Try it and see what happens."

For three nights in a row Caro came to the club, checking supplies and figures, then singing with the band. J.T. accompanied her every night, always making his presence known, even though he stayed out of her way. He watched every move she made but kept his opinions on what she said and did to himself. During the days they discussed any and every topic, any topic except the one issue they both skirted as if it were poison: the baby.

On the third night she sang a song about love gone wrong and the last note trembled in the air before a burst of applause echoed to the rafters. J.T. leaned against the far wall, his arms crossed, as he watched Caro perform for the late crowd. The audience was made up mostly of tourists pretending to be cowboys for a week or two of vacation. A few, he was sure, were Salt Lake City residents who drove over simply to rub elbows with the rich who could afford to stay in the sleepy resort town.

He watched her sing, his eyes never leaving her face as she slowly swayed to the sad music of another song about a dying love affair. She was just as different as Mike had promised. J.T. had originally been bent simply on conquering her, only to find himself wanting her cute little body as close to his as he could get it. Now. It had been that way ever since he had first seen her in the restaurant: an instant recognition of souls. He smiled grimly at his own poetic thoughts. This was an alien feeling to him, one he didn't like. It seemed to take the control of the situation out of his hands. He had just been leading her on in the beginning, trying to frighten her by teaching her a lesson. Instead he was being taught . . . but he seemed to be a slow pupil lately. Frustration rose in him, almost blocking his breathing. He had to get hold of himself and remember what it was he was doing there. He'd leave at the end of the week, after teaching her a lesson and himself a little restraint. That was it. All he needed was a little restraint.

A hand reached up to help Caro off the stage. The young man's arm went around her waist, staying there much too long as he guided her to his companions' table in the center of the room. She was a trophy to show off to his friends. J.T. remained where he was, propped against the wall, with a clear view of both her and the table.

Caro glanced up to mentally lock horns with him. A small, cruel smile played about his lips, telling her that he already knew her game and was amused by it. That only fueled her anger. She gave a friendlier smile than she had intended to the young man by her side and was rewarded with a tighter squeeze on her waist as his eyes lit up.

The young man sat down next to Caro at the table, ordering the bartender to bring a round of drinks. Jess, behind the bar, gave a shrug and filled the order, afraid to look at the boss lady for fear of breaking out in a grin and ruining the young man's act.

Caro stayed for a few minutes' conversation before deciding to call it quits. The taste of vengeance was sour and her emotions were deflated. No matter what she did or how much she flirted, J.T. merely grinned as he watched her make a fool of herself. She shouldn't care what he thought, anyway. After all, he was no more than an employee. . . .

As she rose to leave, however, so did the young man at her side.

"Wait a minute, pretty lady. Where are you going?" he slurred, bending too close to her for comfort, his sour whiskey breath repelling her. She placed a hand on his chest to help him keep his distance.

Suddenly she was tired of playing games, especially those she played alone. She had seen a few of the single women approach J.T. and he had shrugged them off, continuing to watch her with smoldering dark eyes that seemed to be connected to her nerves with invisible strings, lightly tugging, pulling her glance back to him.

"It's been fun, but I'm afraid it's over for the evening. Thank you for the drink." She turned to the rest of the men at the table. "It was nice to have met you. Enjoy yourselves." Caro made her way around the tables and chairs, not realizing until she reached the entrance that the young man was following her.

"Honey, I'm going home with you," he muttered, his hand once more snaking around her waist. "Finders keepers, and I found you." His breath was heavy against her skin, his touch hot and clammy.

"I'm sorry, but this is where we part company. Go back to your friends and enjoy yourself." Her voice was cool and businesslike, her manner totally reserved. She was used to handling this type of situation.

"But you're my present for being a good boy." His voice was almost a whine. "Why, I came here just to meet you. You can't turn me away."

"I just did." She gave a small shrug and continued

to walk to the door. Sam waited for her at the entrance. As usual, he was keeping a close eye on her. But the young man didn't realize that, as evidenced by his persistence.

"Just a minute," he said, his voice turning nasty. "I bought you drinks. The least you could do is let me see you home."

That did it! She turned to face him, her dark eyes turning electric. "Just a minute. You bought me one drink. That's all! But even if you had bought me a dozen drinks, I still wouldn't have to let you see me home." Her forefinger tapped repeatedly on his chest for emphasis. "Do you understand?"

It wasn't until he heard the soft clapping behind him and saw J.T.'s broad shoulders beside him that the young man realized that the entire embarrassing episode had been witnessed.

"Consider yourself told, mister." J.T. spoke quietly, but his slightly tensed body was a warning in itself.

The young cowboy muttered an epithet under his breath, then turned on his heel to rejoin his friends.

"And you," J.T. narrowed his angry gaze at Caro, "are coming with me. Home. Now." She began to protest, but he held up his hand to silence her. "No sass. Just move."

The short drive home was quiet. Caro tried to keep her anger alive with the thought of him standing behind her, ensuring that she came to no harm. Sam had been there to take care of her, she knew. But what if he hadn't been? Occasionally they had gotten busy enough for him to be far from the front of the bar.

Wait a minute! What was she doing? She wouldn't

even have been in that mess if it hadn't been for Joseph! Why was she justifying his actions when it was all his fault that she had been trying to make him jealous?

When he took her arm to help her out of the pickup she suddenly wished she were taller, heavier, and a lot stronger. Then she'd be able to shove him, hard, and feel immense satisfaction as she watched him sprawl in the street. But she wasn't any of those things and it was almost all she could do just to keep up with him as he "walked" her to the front door.

He made his way directly to the kitchen, his anger showing itself by the way he slammed the kettle down on the stove.

"Don't you ever drink coffee?" she asked, her voice higher than usual, restrained aggression showing in the way her hands were clenched on her hips.

"No, I hate coffee. I drink tea." He reached for a cup and the box of tea bags, flinging open the lid to stare down at the offending packets. "I also happen to love loose tea, which you don't seem to have. Why?"

"I don't know. It seems so sissified, somehow. I can't imagine you liking it. I always thought of it as a woman's drink."

"You *what?*" he roared, his dark chocolate brown eyes bigger than she had ever seen them before. "By damn! That's it! I've had just about as much as I can stand. I've been watching you sashay around here and I've continued to play the gentleman, even when it drove me crazier than I can say. Then, tonight, you pushed me almost to the brink by flirting with that wimp in the bar, and now you attack my masculinity!"

Caro backed up, slowly edging through the doorway and toward the stairs. If she could just make it to her room, she could shove the chair under the doorknob. But J.T. came toward her, matching her step for step.

"I've been patient, more patient than I have ever been before in my life. I thought you were emotionally young, too inexperienced to know what you were doing. I believed all that drivel you've been handing me for the past several days. I imagined that your attorney, my best friend, really knows the type of person you are and thought if I could just have patience . . ." His words were a growl from deep in his throat, spoken as much for his own benefit as for hers. His hands clenched and unclenched at his sides, not reaching for her yet, but ready to do so the moment he decided it was time. "What you really need is a man who's stronger than you are. Someone to overpower that strong personality and that perfectly formed body. You need me, no doubt about it."

He struck with the swiftness of a cobra, locking her arms in a viselike grip. Her gasp was the only sound she made. Her stumbling feet halted their backward travel and glued themselves to the floor. His eyes glistened with a macabre but humorous light as he watched her as a scientist would study an amoeba he had trapped under a microscope.

"J.T., please let go. You're hurting me," she murmured softly, imploring him, almost afraid to speak louder in case he became more upset. Her pulse beat at an almost unbelievable rate, the blood coursing through her veins to bring a sheen of perspiration to her heated skin.

"Now," he muttered hoarsely, "I'm going to make love to you now."

"No, wait," she protested, suddenly both frightened and excited at the same time.

"Now."

He had her in his arms and up the stairs before she even realized what was happening enough to struggle against his grip. She didn't really want to. Somehow she knew she had been pushing him, fighting him, hoping for just this reaction. She had wanted him to overpower her and take responsibility for the decision out of her hands. She had wanted him to take over, to take *her* over, and make love to her. She suddenly needed his hands on her, over her, touching, caressing, exploring. And her hands itched with the need to touch him in the same way.

Her slender arms found their way around his neck, her long nails digging into his nape and scalp, raking through the vitality of his dark hair. His eyes burned down into hers, his step faltering at her bedroom door.

"Don't change your mind," she whispered pleadingly.

He shook his head slowly, still studying her with his dark chocolate brown eyes. "I won't. Not now. Not ever." He said the words as if they were a promise.

He stood her by the side of the bed. They

devoured each other with their heated gazes before
J.T. slowly, lightly caressed her cheek before moving
on to the first of her blouse buttons. As if on
cue, Caro did the same. They undressed each other,
his hands fumbling with the buttons of her shirt
every time she fumbled with his. They undid each
other's belts, then reached for the snaps of each other's jeans. Their hands tested the texture of each
other's skin, the tautness, the firmness, the softness,
the nearness. . . .

They melded together, arms and legs sensuously
entwined, as J.T. finally moved to ease her torture
and stretched her out on the wide bed. Both her
hands were captured by one of his, then imprisoned
high above her head. His eyes turned brilliant as they
slowly but thoroughly explored her totally bared
body, seeking and finding a mole here, a dimple
there.

"Don't look at me like that." Her throat closed as
her emotions warred with each other.

"Why?"

"Because you'll find something wrong with me,"
she finally admitted.

"Never." His voice was like warm water running over her tensed flesh. "Even your faults are
lovely."

He kissed her ear, her arched throat, his lips
trailing down her shoulder and then her arm. She felt
him tremble with passion and a light, airy feeling of
wonder encompassed her.

She itched to touch him as intimately as his lips
were touching her, to feel the muscles below his skin

stretch and bunch. She needed to absorb his strength through her palms. "Let go of me," she pleaded in a hoarse whisper, awed at the responses he was pulling from her.

"No."

"I want to touch you."

"No. Not yet." His mouth was against her breast, his warm breath teasing her already taut nipple, his rough tongue tempting it to attention.

"Why? Why can't I touch you?"

"Because I know what will happen." His words were almost lost against her white skin. "Hush." He stroked her side down to her hip, his fingertips heated against the coolness of her flesh. Then his hand slowly worked its way back up her side to rest just under her soft, quivering breast. "Hush."

A strange lethargy so overpowered her that her lids drooped closed and she allowed him to immerse her in the sensations he aroused by touch alone.

"You're beautiful." His hand trailed molten heat over her thigh and crested over her softly rounded abdomen. "So very beautiful."

She arched her back again, silently begging for the relief of touching him. Still he wouldn't let her arms go.

His lips touched one spot, stopped to explore another, his head moving ever downward. His body shivered and suddenly he freed her hands and held her close to him, hugging her until she conformed intimately to his own very masculine contours.

She gave a light sigh, reveling in being able to touch him at last. It was as good as she had thought it would be. His body was firm beneath her hand, his skin taut and solid and hard. Her palms glanced over him as if she were reading him in braille, finding contours and basking in the difference between his and hers. He continued to teach her, taking her hands and guiding them as his own continued to travel her body.

Ever since she had met him she had wondered what it would be like to make love to him. She faced that fact now. When he had told her that he wanted to make love to her she had agreed only because she had known that, for the very first time in her life, that was what she wanted, too.

"Do you like me to touch you here? Here? What about here? Does that please you, Caro?" He whispered away all her fears and made her bolder in return. "Tell me, Caro, tell me . . . and I'll tell you."

She murmured her shy answers and he understood. The emotional connection, the strong bond between them, surpassed even their physical passions.

When he took her in total possession, Caro was more than ready. She cried out for him and he answered as man always has, with his thrust of ownership, branding her as his with actions that needed no words. And she responded by allowing him to conquer her in the age-old action. It was a heady rise to unknown heights before a slow descent to earth.

"Good," he murmured into the softness of her hair as he held her to him. "It was good."

Caro didn't speak. She was held securely in

the cradle of his arms, and nothing less than an earthquake would remove her from his caring comfort.

Tired, they slept, she with one hand tangled in the mat of hair on his chest and he clasping a small, firm breast in the palm of his hand.

4

~~~~~~~~~~~~~~

Large, slightly roughened hands woke her from slumber, silently urging her body to drift somewhere between the real world and a champagne-soft dream world.

Husky words were whispered in her ear. "I need you again."

Firm lips traveled on satin-smooth skin to tease pliable contours hidden by the dark.

Images of the night before and the wicked, wonderful things he had done flashed through her mind, then connected somehow with his stroking, erotic caresses to blend into physical perfection.

A small noise just slightly louder than a sigh passed from her throat to ease through her mouth. No other words were needed.

He took her with the same tenderness as before, but this time his hands were more knowing, infinitely more subtle in their approach.

It was even more wonderful the second time. And more frightening, because she wanted him so much.

When the Utah sun broke over the mountains and lit the valley floor, Caro was just waking. She immediately realized that the warmth that had been close to her all night was gone. Her eyes remained closed while her hand searched the empty bed anyway. But it was true, he was gone.

She raised her head, already sensing that he wasn't in the bedroom or the bathroom. Everything was silent.

She could see Mike Avery's face when she had first told him about her wish to find a man who would give her a child. He had been incredulous, then angry. Then he had begun telling her of the perils of tackling something as intimate as that topic. But it had worked. Last night had proven to her that two people, with care and tenderness, could conceive a child. She frowned. She needed a copy of the contract J.T. had signed. The future was too iffy to rely on a man's conscience and sense of fair play. He might be willing to relinquish all rights now, but would he always feel that way? She hoped so. Joseph would probably be thankful, too, to have a copy. He would undoubtedly want proof that he would be under no obligation to her or her child.

Caro put her hands behind her head and stared out the window at the beautiful Utah mountains. Joseph. He was perfect. He was wonderfully considerate and totally attentive, if the previous night had proved anything. Charming and masculine, as the women in The Loose Noose would have been able to testify. And he was virile. He was, in fact, fantastic!

And she seemed to want him as much as he wanted her. It was a crazy sort of emotional pull that had controlled her from the moment she had seen him in the restaurant in Salt Lake City. Was this what women meant when they said it was fate that had brought them together with their mates? Was her meeting with J.T. something that had been arranged by the gods to show her that she needed to know an emotional commitment before she could bring another tiny person into the world?

Her smile drifted away as she faced the real problem: She was *too* emotionally connected to him. It was the first time she had ever felt that way about anyone, and the feelings were threatening. She felt as if she were on a backpacking trip without supplies or a map. She didn't know what to do.

Conflicting ideas raced back and forth in her head. He knew that she could afford to raise a child and give it everything it could want. And he also knew where to find her later.

How had she gotten herself into a mess like this? All she had wanted to do was to find a suitable man with whom to have a baby. She hadn't wanted a commitment. Just by watching the members of the various bands drift in and out of what they laughingly referred to as relationships, hadn't she seen enough people fall apart? She didn't want that for herself. It was, she knew, best to rely on no one but yourself, a lesson she had learned early and then had had reinforced over and over. She would just have her baby and never see J.T. ever again. That sounded easy enough, didn't it? But she knew how totally impossible that would be. Nothing was simple

. . . including the puzzle of Joseph and why he had applied for this job in the first place.

He had started out angry with her. But if he had seriously tried to break Brandon Cole's contract she would, in all probability, have let him off the hook immediately. After all, who wanted a reluctant father? But why had J.T. then gone on to volunteer himself? What did he hope to gain?

She gave a sigh and reached for the thermometer the doctor had told her to use daily. She was supposed to keep track of her temperature so she would know the exact time of ovulation. So far she hadn't missed this part of the morning routine. After a moment she checked it and her heart stopped. If her calculations were correct, the time for conception was right now! With any luck at all she could have conceived on her first try. Only she hadn't been trying. She hadn't thought once about having a baby. She had thought only of Joseph, and his hands, and his body. . . .

Stop it! her tortured mind screamed, as vision after vision of their love play filled her mind. It hadn't been making love, it had been *sex!* Sex, pure and simple. She wasn't a Victorian miss, simpering while she waited for the man of her dreams to come along; she was a very contemporary woman who knew her own body and its functions and had finally used them. That was all there was to it.

J.T. waited impatiently for the phone to be picked up. It was finally answered by a groggy young voice. "Brandon? J.T. Get your tail over to Mike Avery's office and pick up the money I left for you. Then pick up Toni, assuming she's still interested in you, and get out of Utah for at least the next year or I might decide to tell Mom and Pop about your 'business dealings.' You got that? Good. Treat Toni right, Brandon. Write the folks monthly and we'll see you in a year. Oh, Brandon? Do something with your life, will you?" Joseph hung up, weary of the whole damned mess with his baby brother.

He crammed his hands into his empty pockets and left the pay telephone outside the motel to begin the long walk back to Caro's house.

He was a fine one to tell Brandon how to lead his life. Look at the mess he was in. He groaned audibly. First he threw a fit in his attorney's office, then he propositioned a girl into thinking he was interested in letting her have his baby. To make matters worse, he had followed Caro, invaded her home, lost his temper, gotten aroused, and taken her to bed. And he still hadn't explained his relationship with Brandon to her. Things had just gotten out of hand too quickly. He had done everything contrary to what he had originally set out to do!

He kicked a rock and sent it hurtling far ahead along his path. What he didn't want to face were his emotions about this fiasco. He had never felt such a strong pull toward anyone as he'd experienced in the past week with Caro. It was as if a ton of lead invaded his legs every time she entered the room. He felt tongue-tied and clumsy and his hands constantly itched to touch her. Sometimes he didn't even care whether he touched her in love or in anger, as long as his fingers could slide across her smooth skin, could feel the melting honey of her flesh. His stomach knotted at the thought. His pulse rate rose. His step quickened.

She was waiting for him at the house.

Caro felt embarrassed. It wasn't because he was sitting in the kitchen and watching her cook breakfast. And it wasn't because his shirt fitted his massive shoulders and chest like a coat of green paint. It was because of his hands. She glanced over her shoulder and watched him play with the salt and pepper shakers. His hands were large, tanned, his fingers long and supple. Her skin tingled as she remembered the sensuous secret spots he had stroked both the night before and that morning. She wanted him to do it again. She wanted *him*. She busied her own hands. She had never felt this way before with anyone, and once more she felt control of her life slipping away from her.

She continued to cook, something she hadn't done in ages. Somehow, despite her confused feelings, it had seemed right that she fix his breakfast while he sat and watched. It was the way she had always imagined a real family would act. . . .

"Caro?" He said her name absently, concentrating on the exact position of the salt shaker. "What would happen if you didn't become pregnant right away? Would you continue to try?"

She stiffened. Was he ready to leave her so soon? Was that the reason he had left so early that morning? Was he already bored with her? She ignored the pain that idea brought. She answered as casually as she could. "I don't know. Why?"

"Because I think we ought to know each other

better before conceiving a child. I need to feel that our child will be well cared for for the rest of its life, and I think you need to know me better to make sure you can live with my child for the rest of your life and not regret your decision."

Caro's back was toward him. She deftly flipped the eggs over, but her other hand turned white with the tightness of her grip on the frying pan. "I think that's a good idea." She hoped her voice sounded light enough. "In fact, you're absolutely right. We'll wait a while." She slipped the eggs out of the pan and onto a bright yellow plate. After adding two strips of bacon and a toasted English muffin, Caro placed it in front of him. "Besides, Mike said he wanted to see you again."

J.T. picked up his napkin and placed it on his lap. "That's right," he said in a voice that was as casual as hers. "Mike said that there were some additional things that needed our okay. We'll remedy that today."

She broke two more eggs and poured them into the frying pan. "I'll call him and get everything set up." But stay, her mind pleaded with him in silence. Stay for a while. . . . She glanced over her shoulder and looked hungrily at him, only to find him staring at her with equal hunger in his eyes. She smiled slowly, hesitantly. And he smiled back. She knew he was going to stay. At least for a while . . .

"Do you enjoy hiking?" J.T. asked, attempting to look composed as he caught his breath. They had been walking what Caro insisted was her usual route, but J.T. didn't believe that anyone could walk everywhere uphill. Wasn't there a downhill some-where?

She chuckled. "This isn't hiking, this is walking. Don't you walk in Salt Lake City?" She leaned back against one of the roadside boulders, turning her face toward the sun and closing her eyes. She was totally content.

"I lift weights, I swim, but this is something new. Everything is uphill."

"It only seems that way. Less than a quarter of a mile more and we'll start descending toward the house. I usually do this in the evening, when the sun is just setting." Her eyes twinkled with humor. "Today I decided to go early and you just had to come with me."

"And when we return home we climb the steps to get to the front door," he muttered. "You'd better be in good shape, or woe is you." A thought seemed to disturb him. "Caro, how will you manage with a baby to carry? Everything is up and down here. Aren't you afraid of losing your balance?"

"I've walked these paths for the past four or five years and know them fairly well. But," she hesitated, "if I decide to have a baby, I'll be very careful. Most women would." She smiled lazily toward the sun. "All a woman has to use is common sense."

"Right, except that I don't think you know the meaning of the term," he muttered, his voice a low growl that showed more emotion than he wanted to.

"Of course I do. I use common sense all the time. That's how I got where I am today." Her smile turned into a smirk. She was successful, that much was fact. Common sense had to have something to do with that.

"Wrong," he corrected her. "Darling, a wonderful voice and Sam's good sense got you where you are today."

She was suddenly alert, the adrenaline pumping hard through her blood as if she were readying for a fight. "Wrong!" she mimicked. "For your information, it was my money that built The Loose Noose, and my decorating ideas and my choice of bands that made it popular. Sam backed me with moral support, and a lot of labor and even more love, but Sam or not, I would have had The Loose Noose or something like it."

J.T. watched the fire in her eyes, marveling at her beauty instead of paying attention to her words, as he should have. But he heard the last sentence. "I believe you, I believe you, I believe you. And if decibels make might right, I believe you again!"

Her brown eyes widened as she realized just how loudly she had been shouting. The air echoed with her words.

"I'm sorry. I don't usually lose my temper that way." Her apology wasn't as sincere as it should have been, but she honestly believed that he was the one at fault.

"And I accept your apology, even though you didn't mean it," was his laughing answer as he placed a kiss on the tip of her nose. Before she could utter another word he began walking again and she had no recourse but to follow.

After a few moments of silence Caro decided that it was time for her to learn more about the prospective father of her child. She tried to ignore the quickening in the pit of her stomach at the thought of the heated passion of his hands on her in the cold dark of night. She refused to admit to the tingling in her breasts as she remembered the way his sensuous mouth and burning tongue had teased her into losing all her inhibitions.

She cleared her throat, casting a sideways glance at him, only to find him staring down at her, a small smile lifting the corners of his mouth.

"What do you do for a living?" She croaked out the words.

"I thought I told you. I'm a certified public accountant."

"You did. I forgot. Does your boss give you a lot of time off, or are you on vacation?"

"I own my own company. If I had an ounce of sense I'd head for Salt Lake City to see what my staff is doing."

Her throat closed. "Then why don't you? You invited yourself here, remember?"

His hand circled the soft upper flesh of her arm, then tightened slightly. They stopped at the side of the deserted road and he turned her toward him as he searched her face. It had a closed, shuttered look, just as he had known it would.

"I'm staying because I want to. I'm staying because you want me to. I'm staying and that's final." His voice was rough yet velvety, teasing, but with just a hint of determination to let her know that he was speaking the truth. When her eyes rose to lock with his, a small, sheepish grin lit her face.

"I know." She spoke softly. "I was playing games and that wasn't fair."

His grin answered hers. "I know you know. I also know it's a good thing we're outside or I just might strip you bare right here for teasing the hell out of me."

She teased him further. "Who, sir? Me, sir?"

Her hands rested lightly on his hips, just as his rested on hers. She allowed the tip of her tongue to peek out between her teeth, suddenly shaken with the craving for his mouth to cover hers, his hands to mold the softness of her breasts.

"Caro," he growled, "you're asking for something you're not ready for."

"How do you know?"

"I'm trying to use a little restraint, but it's not easy." His eyes followed the path her tongue made, his hands clenching on her hips, unconsciously pulling her forward to meet the thrust of his legs. She looked up and got a better view of his emotions as his eyes changed color. They had been dark, but as he pulled her closer they became almost golden, toasty in color, warming as his thoughts matched his actions. Her supple body leaned against his hardness, bending and willowy and giving.

"Do you even wear high-heeled jogging shoes?" he questioned, knowing he should be concentrating on something other than his immense urge to take her there and then.

"Yes. They're called wedgies and they make me tall enough to see you better," she whispered. Her eyes were answering more than his question.

"How far is the house?" His voice was a harsh whisper.

"Over the next hill and down a block," she whispered in return.

He took her hand in his and began almost running. "How fast can you walk?"

She giggled as she tried to keep up with him. He was in far better shape than she had originally thought. "Apparently not fast enough."

"You're right, Ms. Businesswoman. And when I give you what's coming to you, just remember that you asked for it."

"I hope so, J.T.," she teased again.

"Don't say another word," he threatened. "Not another word until I get you home, or you may not make it there."

They made it, barely.

The door wasn't quite shut when J.T. turned and took her in his arms, crushing her to him as if he would never let her go. "Kiss me. Hold me, Caro."

"I am, J.T.," she murmured, her hands reaching to caress the sides of his jaw as her mouth covered his, taking the initiative.

"You finally called me J.T.," he murmured into the palm of her hand. "I must have broken down another barrier."

"Too many to count," she confessed breathlessly as his tongue erotically touched the spaces between her fingers.

"Touch me," he moaned.

"How, J.T.?" She taunted him as he had done her the night before. "Do you like it when I touch you here? And here? Do you?"

"Yes. Yes to everything," he muttered before giving in to the urges that always came over him in her presence. They melted into each others arms, savoring each other's touch before finding their way onto the cushioned softness of the couch in the living room. Sunlight streamed in and warmed their skin as they took pleasure in giving.

Caro recorded a mental image of him as she felt his tapered torso, his broad shoulders, filing it away in her memory for another day when she would want to savor his nearness when he wasn't there. A strange sadness flooded her even as he tenderly made love to her.

His hand tightened on her bottom, bringing her back to awareness of him as their hips swung in unison to a rhythm that was the same in both of them. It was all the invitation she needed to belong to him and she became bold, igniting a heat in him that consumed them both.

It was dark before Caro realized just how hungry she was. While J.T. was in the shower she slipped downstairs, humming a child's tune. Something light would do for the evening meal; after all, her culinary skills weren't that great.

She heard his step on the stairs before she saw him and her heartbeat quickened.

"Soup's on! And I mean literally," she chimed, holding up a pan filled with canned chicken noodle soup.

"Sound's better than a burnt offering," he teased, but his eyes weren't twinkling as they usually did when he joked.

"J.T.? Are you feeling all right? Did our walk tire you out?" She blushed as she realized just how silly that last question was.

She was rewarded with a rumbling chuckle. "Believe me, Caro, it wasn't the walk that did me in." He walked toward her, cornering her near the stove.

She turned, placing the pan back on the burner before she spilled the soup. Her hands had started trembling at his nearness. Surely he knew just how much of a gibbering idiot she became whenever he was around.

"It was you. You turned me inside out with your eyes and hands." His lips caressed the side of her neck. "Your soft little body wore me out." His arms encompassed her waist, one hand resting on the lower softness of her abdomen to set off a fire somewhere in her veins.

"Are you sure it was *my* soft little body?" Her voice sounded husky even to her own ears.

He stilled. "What do you mean?"

"I mean, wouldn't any body have done?" Please, she prayed, let him answer without playing games.

"Are you fishing for compliments?"

"No."

"Are you playing games?"

"No."

"Then don't ask questions that have obvious answers," he growled. "I wouldn't have made love to you just to give myself something to do. I wouldn't have half-run back here just to throw anyone on the couch and ravish her. Give me some credit for taste and discrimination."

Tears flooded her eyes, but she didn't want to give

him the satisfaction of seeing them fall. His words had satisfied her at least as much as they had hurt.

He gave a deep sigh. "I made love to you for the same reason you made love to me," he explained softly in her ear. "And I'm sure you don't go around dragging men into your bed, do you?"

"No, but . . ."

"No buts about it. I am not an animal who needs to have a woman, no matter who, three times a day." His chuckle echoed in her ear. "I won't say that there wasn't a time, when I was about nineteen, when any girl who could form the word yes didn't stand a chance of spending the night alone, but those days are over, thank goodness."

"And now you're more discriminating?" she asked softly.

"And now I go for quality instead of quantity," he corrected. "And, lady, you're quality."

She took a deep breath and found enough courage to face him. "Then why the sad look in your eyes when you entered the room? You should have been sated, satisfied, and yet you looked as if you were saying good-bye."

"Because just this morning we agreed to get to know each other, and there I was, practically forcing you onto your own . . . uh . . . couch in the middle of the day."

"Oh," she said softly, her eyes turning to warm liquid silver. She reached up to encircle his neck, her hands cupping the back of his head. "You're absolutely right. We really should learn restraint. From now on we'll play cards and dance and talk about records and books. We'll see the countryside and discuss dogs and cats and the differences between the two. And we'll each be waiting for the other to make the move that we both wanted to make anyway."

"You're brazen and wanton and sexy, and I think I need you again." His warm breath caressed the side of her cheek while his hand cupped her bottom to bring it closer to the heart of his problem.

"You don't know for sure?" she teased breathlessly.

"I know. I was just feeling you out," he growled. "Literally."

"Don't stop." She was breathless.

"I promise I won't."

And he didn't.

His voice echoed in her ear. "What does a guy have to do to get a balanced meal around here?"

Caro stretched lazily, tantalizing J.T. with her slim, taut, naked body. "Most people either go to restaurants or cook for themselves. I'm all in favor of cooking if someone would keep his hands off me for an hour or so." The tip of her tongue darted out to seek the hard bud on his chest, making him suck in his breath, his gold-flecked eyes staring down at her possessively.

"And I'll be more than happy to keep my hands off you if you promise not to drive me to distraction. I may not be a teenager in the prime of his sex life, but I'm certainly not over the hill yet, if my reaction to you is anything to go by."

"Oh?" she said innocently. "Do I distract you?" Her tongue darted out for another foray, her small hand resting on the firmness of his hip, drifting from there to his waist. Suddenly his words registered and her hand stilled. "J.T.? How old *are* you?"

He gave a heavy sigh. "I guess the time has come to 'fess up. I'm thirty-two."

Relief flowed through her body, warming her. "Is that all? My word, I thought you were going to say twenty-five or twenty-seven, or something equally awful."

"Oh, thirty-two doesn't bother you, is that it? Well, just remember this. When I was twelve and my voice began to change, you were a sophisticated teenager of fifteen." She giggled at the thought. "And when I was barely seventeen and starting to shave every day, you were a wordly woman of twenty. And when I was twenty-eight and just beginning my own business, you were already thirty-one and established. And when I'm a charming sophisticated gentleman of forty-eight you will be . . ." His voice lowered and roughened as his mouth burrowed into the soft sweetness of her neck. "Just right. Just like you are right now."

Her breath caught in her throat at the wonder of her intensely passionate emotions. In such a short time he had filled a huge and hitherto unknown cavity in her life with fun, companionship and enchantment, leaving her hard pressed to remember what it had been like when she was alone. It was as if he had always been with her. He had given her so much, yet she couldn't speak of it. She couldn't put her feelings for him into words or she might show more of her private thoughts than she could ever be comfortable with. It was time, once more, to remain silent. But that didn't mean she couldn't enjoy the wonder of it all. She snuggled closer.

"Do you know what I want?" he whispered in her ear, his magical fingers tantalizing one breast.

"What?" she whispered in return.

"Dinner," he growled, and she laughed, pulling the sheet away from the bed and wrapping it around her sarong style before getting up.

"What did you do that for?" He leaned back, totally relaxed and comfortable as he lay stretched out and exposed.

"I've always seen it done in the movies and I wanted to try it," she lied, not willing to tell him that she felt wonderful lying beside him naked, but was too self-conscious to walk across the room that way.

"I hope you enjoy making beds and tearing them apart, because that's what I see in your future." He sounded amused, yet touched that she could still have such inhibitions.

"What I see in the future," she called from the bathroom, "is dinner. How about T-bone steaks and baked potatoes with creamed cauliflower and hot rolls?"

"Ummm, sounds delicious. What time do we eat?" he asked as he stood and stretched lazily.

She almost forgot what she was going to say as she watched him. He was a magnificently built man, with broad shoulders and rippling biceps. The dark hair on his chest formed a vee down his flat belly and further, like an arrow. His legs were strong and sturdy, covered with dark hair. She glanced back up, only to be caught staring.

"We dine as soon as you're dressed. We're eating

next door to The Loose Noose." Her mouth lifted in a dimpled smile as she watched him. But a small twinge of guilt niggled at her brain. Shouldn't she be cooking for him? Wasn't that what a woman was supposed to do?

He chuckled. "I should have known."

"Well, I'm just as tired and worn out as you are. And since neither one of us wants to cook, I see no harm in indulging ourselves with someone else's efforts," she retorted defensively, feeling guilty that she wasn't cooking for him.

"I hadn't thought of it that way, but you're right, lady," he answered, unconcerned with her reaction. "Lead the way."

5

J.T. spent the next week with Caro and it was a glorious, wonderful week. But work, both his and hers, continued to intrude on their lives. On Tuesday Caro argued with the man who was surveying her Snowhawk property before building a large concrete and wood fence around the back. J.T. stood by, patiently waiting for her to get off the phone so he could use it.

"We've got to stop meeting this way," he muttered as she put the receiver down and he picked it up.

"Wait! I'm not finished yet. I still have other calls to make."

"And you have an office you can go to. I'm here and can't get to mine." His expression turned from stern to sheepish. "Of course I can get to my office. It's only forty miles down the road!" he exclaimed, softening as he took in her stricken look. "I've been so wrapped up in your corner of the world that I almost forgot about mine."

"I thought you were going to stay here," she said when she finally found her voice. "Or was that only when I said I wanted you to leave?"

"Are you telling me that you want me to stay now?" His hands went to her waist, forcing her to continue to look into his dark chocolate brown eyes.

"It means that I don't care, I just want to know what your plans are for future reference. After all, we both have lives to lead. I need to plan ahead," she lied, hoping that she wasn't giving away the panic she felt at the thought of him leaving. Thoughts tumbled over each other, confusing her. How could she care so much whether he stayed or left? How could she have become so involved with someone after only a few weeks of knowing him? Her earlier experiences told her to ignore their strange mental connection with each other, for as surely as the sun rose at daybreak he would leave her one day and she would once again be the odd man out. "As a matter of fact, I think it's a wonderful idea. We should call this whole thing off. You and I should both get back to our own lives," she said coldly. "So, if you'll kindly take your hands off me, I'll get back to work and let you get back to your packing."

His hands remained where they were, caressing the sides of her face as he studied her. "I'm only leaving for the day, so I don't need to pack. I'll be back by dinnertime." His voice was low and gentle, as if he realized that she was frightened of this new change in their tenuous relationship. He couldn't quite understand why she should be so frightened, but he'd find out in time. He'd make her open up enough to tell him.

"I think you ought to leave. Period," she said stubbornly, refusing to give in to the soft, cajoling tone of his voice.

"We'll discuss this over dinner tonight. Right now, I'm going to my office. I'll call Mike Avery while I'm in town and have lunch with him. If you need me you can reach me at either place."

Before she could answer, his lips came down on hers, muting any retort she might have considered making. His lips were cool, firm. His tongue sought admission, finally winning as she slowly opened to him. He was silently telling her of his commitment, but still she worried. How long would he go on returning from his own territory to play second fiddle in her neck of the woods? Not for long, she'd bet, although she would be a fool to force him back into his own life when she wanted him so much in hers.

His lips reluctantly left hers and he turned, walking toward the door, a satisfied smile on his face as he spoke over his shoulder. "I'll be back in time for dinner. See you then. Oh, and wear a smile, will you?"

"Anything else?" she asked sarcastically.

He stopped halfway up the stairs and grinned down at her. "No. A smile should be sufficient. Clothing would only get in the way."

Then he was gone. And she was standing in the hallway, a hand covering her smile.

* * *

"I'm sorry," she said haughtily. "I don't happen to care for liver and onions *or* kidneys in tomato sauce."

"I understand," he said with equanimity. "I don't care for macaroni and cheese. It's the small things we have to work out and compromise on."

"I can't see compromising on likes and dislikes. They're a very definite matter of taste and have been established over a period of years, thirty-two in your case and thirty-five in mine."

"And I say that although some of our tastes may vary, others will complement each other." He lifted a forkful of green beans to his mouth.

"I disagree. Besides, I won't cook every evening. This isn't my vocation in life."

"It isn't mine, either, Caro, but I'm willing to share the workload with you." His tone was reasonable, soothing her ruffled feathers.

But still she pushed. "I'll let you do your share for the remaining two weeks that you're here."

One craggy brow rose. "Are you setting a time limit? What happens if you're not pregnant by then?" he asked smugly before he took another bite of roast, then waited patiently for her answer.

"I'll contact you if I need you to . . . ah . . . to ah . . ." Her voice dwindled away, her face blushing a brilliant red. Thirty-five years old and she *still* couldn't discuss sex!

"If you'll need me to stand at stud again?" He seemed composed, but Caro knew that there was an intense anger simmering deep down inside him. It showed in his chocolate brown eyes and tightened jaw muscles. Suddenly her own anger bloomed.

She smiled sweetly. "Exactly."

"How kind. Perhaps you can recommend me to a few of your friends. With your help I could be rich in no time." His voice was no longer calm. It was hoarse, filled with emotion and much deeper in tone.

Suddenly Caro realized just how much they were hurting each other. And for what? Because they had agreed to come together for a few weeks and part as distant friends afterward? How crazy could she get! She was angry with him for acting like the type of person she had wanted him to be!

"I'm sorry." Her voice was low. She refused to look at him to see if he would accept her apology.

He didn't. Instead, he threw his napkin down on the table and stood. "Damn it, Caro! You make me so mad, I could . . ." He stalked from the room and out the door, slamming it in his wake and leaving her to stare in open-mouthed wonder at the spot where he had been sitting.

What in heaven's name was his problem?

He came back just before dawn. He fumbled with the door and shuffled unevenly up the stairs to his room. Caro listened quietly, her entire body tense, poised with expectation as she waited for him to open the bedroom door and shout obscenities at her.

Sam had called after midnight and told her that J.T. had spent the night at The Loose Noose being surly to the customers before drinking himself into a blue funk. Then he had walked out of the bar and up the hill toward the ski slopes. Sam had left him alone, knowing that he was in no danger and would find his way home sooner or later. Sam had seemed to understand J.T.'s anger and frustration, which was more than Caro did.

Caro glanced at the illuminated hands of her small alarm clock. Then she dredged around in her mind for the anger she had assumed she would don when he returned, only to find relief instead. What was the matter with her? She should be furious that a guest in her home, a man that she had hired, a . . . a . . . Her mind balked at the next words. Better to ignore the fact that he would be the father of her child. It would be too easy to get used to the idea. Too easy, indeed.

She lay back down and listened to him fumble around in the guest room, grunting just before his shoes hit the floor with a thud, groaning as he fell back on the bed and rattled the headboard against the wall. She'd have to move that bed in the morning. She barely controlled the giggle that was rising in her throat at the picture she was imagining. His clothes would be mussed, his head dizzy and aching, his throat dry. He'd feel miserable after a night of drinking and debauchery and terribly sorry in the morning for allowing his anger to get the best of him.

J.T.'s clothes were mussed; his head was dizzy and aching; his throat was parched and dry. He felt miserable after a night of drinking and debauchery and already terribly sorry for allowing his frustration to get the best of him.

Instead of allowing his anger to control his actions he should have taken hold of her and made passionate love to her all night! He smiled to himself at the thought. He should have shown her exactly who was boss and what that terse but explicit expression meant. He should have taken her in his arms and kissed her until she was limp, although he already knew that once he had her in his arms he would never experience another rational thought again until she was away from him.

He reached over and grabbed the second pillow, placing it by his side. The room was dark. Caro was in the next room sound asleep and for the first time that he could remember, he was wrenchingly lonely for a woman's warm body. Not just any woman. It had to be Caro. But by this time she was probably so angry with him that she'd rather spit on him than have him near her.

His mind settled on that thought. How did he know? He hadn't tried, had he? He rolled to a sitting position, pulling his shirt out of the waistband of his pants. It didn't matter that from the first moment he had met her he had done everything in his power to be calm and cool and composed and *superior,* attempting to show her by deed just how stupid her idea was. All he had succeeded in doing was falling right in with her plans and playing the fool with great expertise.

Damn! He *was* a fool! He stood and shucked his pants, which left him wearing nothing but his dark, tight fitting undershorts. He took a deep breath, hoping the air he breathed was filled with determination. If she woke up and found him with her all she could do was say no, right? Right.

Her door was closed but not locked. The downstairs hall light gave out just enough of a glow to let him enter her room without stumbling around. He stood by the side of the bed and stared down at her, his heart beating heavily. His throat closed. Her golden-blond hair was spread in a shadow around her, the white sheets making her skin a pale gold. She was small and sweet and vulnerable. She was also sassy and stubborn, and J.T. somehow knew that she had been lonely most, if not all, of her life.

Her arm stretched over the empty bed next to her. Without questioning his own motives he held her hand and took hold of the covers, raising them enough so he could slide between the coolness of the percale sheets. Then he placed her slightly cupped hand across his chest. She gave a small sigh in her sleep and turned on her side, instinctively curling against him. He waited, barely breathing, until he was sure she was still asleep, then he carefully maneuvered his arms around her, keeping her as close to him as he had imagined earlier. Her head rested lightly on his chest, just below his chin, and he could smell the fresh scent of her hair and feel the warm softness of her curled body. He, too, gave a sigh of contentment. This was where he wanted to be.

Caro's lashes flitted gently only once. Then a small smile graced the corners of her mouth. This was where she wanted to be.

His body told her that he was impatient. His hands told her that he wanted to sweetly lengthen their time together. A message was transmitted by his touch to her soft, secret places and she returned the message with her own caresses. His skin was warm and smooth, his movements gentle against her. His knees traveled between her legs, spreading her thighs for his entrance. She could feel his pulse throbbing in his throat as she touched him. His hair curled and twined around her fingers.

At first he made love to her with gentleness, then he turned more demanding as they continued. They asked a lot of each other, and received what each had requested as they fulfilled each other.

Afterward he stayed with her. "Am I too heavy?" His mouth was next to her ear, his breathing corresponding with the heartbeat throbbing against her breast.

"No." Her hands continued to caress his back, following the trail of his spine down to the small of his back and up again. How could she convey the wonderful rush of feeling that his staying with her gave? What words would be able to show her appreciation of his caring? None.

"Good. I don't want to leave you."

"Please don't." Her voice was becoming groggy. Sleep was falling over her like a warm, cozy blanket.

"You were awake last night when I came in." His mouth teased the outer shell of her ear, startling her into wakefulness.

"I wasn't."

"Yes, you were."

"No."

"Say no to my face."

"I'd rather say no to your chest." She blew on the hair at his throat before kissing the spot.

"I thought so. An inveterate liar," was all he could say before his lips captured hers in pleasure as he took her again.

He was patient, but even a fool could have seen that his patience was coming to an end. "The entire world is full of compromises, Caro, not just this small corner."

She slammed her book down. "I don't care what the whole world is or does. I've always lived by myself, so I've never had to compromise. And I say that you're getting too bossy."

"Don't get off the subject."

"That happens to *be* the subject." She controlled her temper with all the restraint she had in her. "I've already broken several of the rules I set for myself by allowing you to be here. Now I want to abide by those rules again, which means that you've got to abide by them, too."

"And if I don't?" He sounded weary and just a touch patronizing.

"If you don't, feel free to leave. I'll be kind and give you twenty-four hours to clear out." Her tone left him in no doubt as to her conviction. Her eyes looked like small chips of ice. Only her heartbeat gave away the fact that she was fearful that he would call her bluff.

"All right, Caro," he sighed, running a hand through his hair and across the back of his neck. "Tell me the rules so you can feel better."

"One: You are to tell me ahead of time of your comings and goings."

J.T. nodded.

"Two: You are not to interfere with my housework as long as you're staying here."

He nodded again.

"Three: You are to stay out of my business, both public and private."

His dark eyes lit with mutinous intent for a moment; then suddenly he gave a slight nod. She was afraid to challenge his agreement further.

"Is that it?" he questioned, and she nodded.

"All right." He stood. "Now I'm getting dressed so we can get to the club on time. I think Sam said eight o'clock?" He walked calmly out of the living room and up the stairs, ignoring her rage at the fact that he had agreed to her rules only to turn around and interfere with the running of her club!

She stood at the bottom of the stairs, her clenched hands on her hips. "You don't have to go to the club! That's my area, not yours!"

He turned and stared down at her. She could see the implacable hardness in his eyes.

"You can rest this evening, stay home, watch TV or read a book." She smiled coldly. "After all, you've been commuting all week, you could probably use the rest."

"On the contrary. I need to go out and see people. If you don't want me to go to the club with you, I'll go without you. But make up your mind, Caro, because either way—I'll be at the club tonight."

Her voice practically tore from her throat. "You are the most maddening, arrogant man I've ever met!"

A satisfied look crossed his face before he hid his emotions. "Now, if we could both just act our sexes instead of one of us becoming confused, we'd get along better."

Her brown eyes narrowed. "Just what are you implying?"

"I'm not implying anything, I'm saying it. You need lessons in femininity. You've been in business so long that you've forgotten you're a woman in anything more than the way you dress."

She almost reeled from the impact of his words. They stung more than she would ever admit. He had zeroed in on her one vulnerable spot.

"That's odd," she sneered, "you don't seem to mind my *masculine* ways when you force your way into my bed."

"Force? Check again, Caro. I never forced you; you were always ready. In fact, you begged for it! What amazes me is how you stayed a virgin for so long. You have the emotional makeup of a first-class whore!"

She walked up the three steps that separated them, her trembling legs carrying her in total rage. "A whore! My, my, J.T., what does that make you? You're the one who makes love on command and for a price! Don't they have a name for people like you?"

"Yes." He spoke through clenched teeth. "Idiot. And that's what I am for taking even one minute of your abuse. You're demented and I'm stupid for staying around and watching you make idiots of us both."

Without thinking, Caro raised her hand and slapped his face. Her whole hand stung as she realized what she had done. His cheek immediately turned white, the imprint of her hand standing out a brilliant red.

"By your own set of rules, I should slap you back. What was good enough for me should certainly be good enough for you."

Her large brown eyes were wide with hurt, bewilderment, and unshed tears. She stared up at him, her full bottom lip trembling. "I hate you," she whispered.

"I wish I hated you," he said.

"I have enough for both of us." She turned slowly and walked the rest of the way up the stairs.

Caro stood in the bathroom for a long, long time. She felt all her energy had been drained by their argument. Now that it was over and she was alone, she realized that she deserved what she had gotten.

She turned on the taps and washed her face with cool water.

Why on earth had she insisted that he stay home? Deep down she knew that she wanted him with her, but for some reason she had wanted him to fight for the privilege. For the first time in a long while she was forced to look at herself through someone else's eyes, and she didn't like what she saw.

She knew that she wasn't hurting him as much as she was hurting herself. She had forced him to fight so she could see whether he was worthy of the honor of being with her. Yet she was angry, because his fighting meant that he was closer to her than she wanted him to be. She was frustrated because he wouldn't be manipulated. In short, she was angry with herself for needing him more than she felt she should.

How could he have said that she wasn't feminine when she had never felt so much a woman in her life? J.T. made her feel that way. He made her cheeks glow, her eyes light up, her hips sway seductively when he was in the room. He had done all that and more, and she was terrified that he had that much control over her emotions.

She could—and she would—manage very well by herself, but as long as he was there, the least she could do was treat him with respect. And the first thing she should do was apologize to him.

He was waiting in the kitchen, sipping a cup of tea, when she went down. She watched him from the doorway for a moment, loving the latent strength in his every movement. He was staring out the back door at the mountainside, his profile unmoving and powerful. Yet despite all the power he exuded, he was still sensitive to her wants and needs.

Would his child be the same way? Would his child be solidly built and yet sweet and generous? Her hand went to her stomach, her eyes seeing another vision: a small toddler, just like J.T., strutting around the kitchen before he came and placed his head in his mother's lap to look up at her with golden-flecked brown eyes and a trusting smile. For a moment the picture was so real that she wanted to cry at the deeply felt emotion of it.

"J.T.?" She clasped her nervous hands together.

He rose and turned, his eyes searching hers for some unspoken answer.

"I'm sorry." Her voice was so low that it was almost a whisper.

His smile lit up her heart with its tenderness. "So

am I." He held out one hand to her, palm up. "Can we call a truce?"

She placed her hand in his without hesitation. "Yes, please," she said.

His mouth came down to give her a sweet, slow, chaste kiss on her forehead. "Come on," he said with a slow smile. "Let's get over to the club. And I promise I'll stay out of your way as long as you don't need my help."

"Thank you."

6

~eeeeeeeeee~

Caro's friend and neighbor who lived down the street sat at the table and chatted with Caro and J.T. before The Loose Noose became thick with the evening crowd.

"So how did you two meet?" Brenda sent Caro a knowing look, her bright blue eyes lit with the expectation of a romantic story. J.T. wasn't going to disappoint her.

His brown eyes twinkled. "I walked into a restaurant in Salt Lake City with a beautiful brunette in the hopes of having an enjoyable evening, but I couldn't take my eyes off a solitary, petite, and utterly charming woman across from me." His eyes told Caro that he remembered every small detail. "She was wearing a black dress and her hair was severely pulled back in a very sophisticated style. I told myself that this was the girl I wanted to meet."

Caro had the grace to blush. So he had known

who she was before he introduced himself to her! Or had he?

She smiled sweetly, playing the part assigned to her as she cast a lingering glance at J.T. "Yes, it was as if we were destined to meet that night."

He gave no explicit answer, just nodded slowly in acquiescence, his gaze narrowing as he attempted to second-guess what was on her mind. Finally he seemed to give up and leaned back to play with his beer glass.

His next words dropped like a bomb. "Yes, and now I can't imagine life without her."

"Does that mean congratulations are in order?" Brenda's blue eyes widened. "You must be special to get Caro to say yes. I've been trying to get her to at least date, and that's been a near impossibility! When's the day?"

Caro's mouth dropped open to say never, but J.T. spoke first. "That's up to Caro." He smiled, his hand rubbing sensuously against her arm. "We haven't discussed it yet."

It took her several moments to be able to think of anything else to say. Her mind was a shambles; she was unable to put two coherent words together. A small part of her was traitorously warmed by his implication, but the rest of her wanted to take her chair and hit him directly over the head with it. She would have enjoyed seeing the wood splinter into a thousand different pieces, piercing his tough hide like sharp needles.

Just then J.T. looked up. Her smile worried him more than her anger or dark thoughts. He could understand most of her reactions, but how would she react to the hint of marriage in her future? It would be an understatement to say that she was opposed to the idea. Why else would she go to such lengths to find a surrogate father? To make sure she *never* had to marry. Instinctively he knew that he had to give her some leeway if he were going to rescue this situation—and her—from the jaws of defeat. If truth be known, he had startled himself. But it felt right. He knew that was what he really wanted to do.

He contemplated his glass again. "Caro has decided to have children right away, even though I'm hesitant."

Caro's eyes widened, as did Brenda's. She glanced between the two as if watching a ping pong match. "Oh?"

Caro's eyes flickered with indecision. She didn't know what to say or do to make the situation better. Finally she decided to roll with whatever J.T. said and worry about the consequences later.

"Yes, if we decide that this is what we both want, J.T. has promised to put aside his lucrative career for the sake of our children and help during the day so I can continue my work." She smiled at the astonished look on Brenda's face, not to mention the startled flicker in J.T.'s eyes. "He's going to be such a *wonderful* father." Something inside goaded her to continue the almost comical farce. "And he'll help with the delivery, of course. He doesn't want to miss a thing!" Her thoughts turned to other things he didn't want to miss but that she was sure she could withhold: love in the middle of the day, hot meals, clean clothing, someone who would answer when he spoke . . . all sorts of things!

By this time Brenda was chuckling out loud. "Come on, you two!"

J.T. grinned back. "But it's true, Brenda. May I call you Brenda?" he questioned and received her nod as she waited for him to continue. "I'll help in the delivery and I'm a fine cook and bottle washer." He gave a sweet, longing, just-for-lovers look, ignoring Caro's suspicious eyes.

"I wouldn't know, darling," Caro said in a syrupy tone. "I've never seen you cook or clean bottles."

"But you will, sweetheart. You will," he promised.

Brenda's blue eyes suddenly glistened with challenge. "Well, in that case, let me tell you that I'll be teaching the Lamaze class in the meeting room of the tennis club this winter. If you're really interested in attending, let me have your card and I'll give you a call."

It was J.T. and Caro's turn to be speechless. Caro glanced at J.T. before swinging her gaze back to Brenda. "When did you begin doing that?" Her voice sounded harsh to her own ears and the smile on her lips was as false as her interest. Her glance swung back to J.T. He was calm, silent, and unperturbed.

"About three months ago." She turned to address J.T. "I had my own children that way, as Caro knows. I just decided that I wanted to help others do the same thing. It's really marvelous!" She held out her hand in challenge. "Your card?"

"Fine," he said blandly as he reached for his wallet and extracted a business card.

Brenda reached across the table, her face showing

her disappointment. She had obviously thought she had called his bluff. "You know, Ken wouldn't go through the training with me for my first child. He said he'd wait until they worked the bugs out of the procedure."

"And did they?" Caro leaned back, suddenly feeling as if she had been waiting for something to happen all night. Now it had and she could relax. After all, what else could go wrong?

"Work out the bugs? No—how many bugs can you work out of natural childbirth? He was there for Amy's birth, though. He went through all the training and half the delivery before he fainted." She hesitated for effect. "I was never sure if he planned it that way or if he'd just gotten tired of waiting."

Everyone chuckled. "That's got to be a wonderful experience, though," Caro admitted, her tone just a little envious.

"If it hadn't been, I wouldn't have done it twice, I can tell you that," Brenda confirmed.

A sharp pain twisted in the pit of Caro's stomach and she suddenly stood. "Well, while you two discover the secrets of the universe, I'd better get to work on the books or Sam will get angry." Her smile was short and false. She could feel J.T.'s narrowed eyes focused on her trembling lower lip and she stiffened. "See you and Ken later, Brenda." She nodded curtly. "J.T., I'll call you when I'm through."

He scraped his chair back. "I'm sure Brenda will understand if I want to be with you, darling." He turned his magic smile on the unsuspecting woman. "Won't you?"

The dark-haired girl waved her hand. "Be my guest. I'm just waiting for Ken to arrive. He should be here any minute."

It seemed to take an eternity to cross the floor casually and walk into the office, Caro thought. It even seemed to take her forever to close the door. But once they were inside, before she could say a word, J.T. spoke.

"If I hadn't handed her my card she would have known we had no plans of any kind. If that was the case then you would have given *our* child a black eye he or she doesn't need. This is a small town, Caro, and you need to think ahead. This way, when our relationship doesn't work out I'll be the bad guy and our child won't be an object of scorn."

"Oh, come on!" Caro exclaimed, her eyes almost even with his chocolate brown ones. "I find it a little hard to believe that marriage is necessary in today's world."

"I find it hard to believe that there are still people who are prejudiced against women in business, but I bet you could tell me a few horror stories."

"Women are nowhere near equal in the workplace and you know it! But that has nothing to do with children!"

"Doesn't it? Just because you read about famous people having children without the benefit of wedlock doesn't mean that middle Americans can do it and get away with it."

Caro held her temples, massaging the small tense muscles that seemed to throb all the way down to her high-heeled boots. "Why do you always make me confused? I think I have everything worked out and then you hit me with something else."

His arms came around her, touching her back with mesmerizing strokes. "Because you haven't seen the problem from all angles, honey. But you will. In time, you will," he soothed, his voice low and wonderfully relaxing.

She finally allowed herself to go limp. His hands were doing wondrous things to her back, sending currents of electricity down her spine. She leaned against him, wanting to feel the outline of his strong form, to lean on him emotionally as well as physically. He was good at guiding . . . and she was so tired of being alone.

"J.T.?" she said against his shirt, her voice muffled by the material. Her head seemed to fit perfectly into the crook of his shoulder and neck.

"Hmmmm?"

"Keep holding me. Just keep holding me," she said with a sigh. She reveled in the feeling of his hard body next to her softer one. He was so much stronger physically. Did that mean he was also stronger emotionally? Could he really feel just how lonely she had been all her life, or was he completely impervious to that side of her personality? Was she just spinning wishful daydreams again?

"Caro?"

"Hmmmm?"

"I don't want to startle you, but I'm going to pick you up and walk to the couch. Then I'm going to lay you down." He waited a moment, his hands continuing to soothe her back, waist, and hips. "Ready?"

His teeth worried her bottom lip, his tongue caressed the fullness of it.

"Uh-hmmm," she moaned softly, completely happy with whatever he said.

She was in his arms instantly, but before he turned toward the couch J.T. flipped off the overhead light and sent the room into darkness.

"I bet you do this with all the girls," she said breathlessly.

"All of them," he confirmed with a growl. She knew that he was only teasing, but suddenly she ached to think of him with anyone else.

"Don't tease," she suddenly begged.

"I'm not teasing. I'm totally earnest, Caro. This is the first time for both of us. Starting now."

Her tension slowly eased away as his words caressed her. Then there was no more time for thought as his lips came down to claim hers in possessive ecstasy.

Lightly calloused hands blazed a new trail as they searched her tightly muscled abdomen. Her hands found his and rested on them as he continued his quest. She loved his touch, made more warm and lovely by the knowledge that the two of them had probably created a tiny child there. His hands continued their magic, searching higher to fondle one perfectly shaped breast.

"Oh, Caro, I need you," he muttered into her soft mouth before giving her another kiss. "But not here, not like this." His strong arms encircled her slim body and held her close as he breathed deeply of the scent of her skin, his heart calming bit by bit as it beat heavily against her breast.

"Then talk to me of sane and sensible things." Her voice was light and whispery, her hands unable to stop tracing the corded muscles of his arms and back as he leaned over her, half sitting, half lying next to her.

"Tell me what you were like as a child, Caro. Were you shy? Did your mother spank you often? Did your father bounce you on his knee?"

Caro was surprised when the warmth of their intimate companionship didn't evaporate as it usually did when she was asked about her past. It seemed perfectly natural to be in J.T.'s arms in the velvet darkness of the office, talking of her childhood.

"I *was* shy as a child, but I don't think I knew it at the time. I was turned over to the state when I was three and raised in welfare homes most of my life, so I don't really remember my parents. Supposedly they made a terrible mistake when they married and rectified it by divorcing. Neither one seemed to want a child and they thought I'd have a better opportunity for a happy childhood if they gave me away. But no one signed the necessary papers so someone else could adopt me." She sighed. "Supposedly neither one wanted to take the responsibility of formally giving me up. By the time the welfare board ironed out the red tape with the adoption board, I was too old for someone to adopt. Everyone wanted babies, not gangling girls who were all arms and legs."

His lips teased her chin before he slowly worked his way down to the softly hollowed pulse point at the base of her throat. "What happened next?"

She moved her head to accommodate him.

"Nothing much. I lived with foster parents for a long time."

"How long?" The tip of his tongue found her skin to be the perfect flavor and sent warm chills through the rest of her as he teased the upper swell of her softly mounded breast.

"Until I was fifteen." Her fingers curled into the thickness of his hair.

His head rose at that and she could feel him trying to see her in the darkness. "Fifteen? What happened after that?"

Her whole body tensed and he could feel it. "Shush, baby, don't answer if you don't want to," he murmured, gradually stroking the warmth back into her system.

She shook her head. "I don't want to," she said hoarsely. She had always hidden the memories of fleeing from a home where the two sons had tried to blackmail her into allowing them to maul her young body. And when her foster parents had caught them at it, they believed the lies the boys told. They said that Caro had provoked it. Her foster parents had known the truth but chose to ignore it in order to protect their own children first. That night she had run away. She hadn't realized that it would be just as tough for her on the streets, but she'd learned to take care of herself fast, because that had been the only way to survive.

He continued to cradle her in his arms, stroking the softness of her skin as if she were a child. Finally he sensed that she was calm once more. "Did you know that your skin tastes like a sweetened lemon?" he teased.

"No. Did you know yours tastes like a salted pine cone?" She entered into the spirit of the exchange.

"I think we've both been oversoaping," he chuckled. "Next time I'll take a shower with your soap and you take one with mine. What's your favorite flavor?"

"Chocolate fudge," she answered promptly.

"In that case I'll bathe in fudge."

"That should be interesting, if a bit sticky."

"Oh, it will definitely be sticky . . . and interesting." His voice lowered humorously, rumbling in his chest beneath the palms of her hands. "But if it endears me to you, I'm all for it."

"Why?" She was curious, but not afraid of his answer. He would never commit himself to her. His words were just that, words, a brand of teasing to make her relax. He had a life of his own to lead.

"Because I want you to miss me when I'm gone this week. I want you to count the hours until I return home from a hard day's work. I even want you to miss me so much that you might try some zany recipe from an old cookbook just to see if you can please me."

"Chauvinist!"

He pretended to be hurt. "I didn't mean for you to try cooking every night! Only on occasion. The rest of the time I want you waiting for me at the door with one of those sheer baby-doll gowns on," he answered complacently.

"Is that what you would expect from a wife?" she demanded pertly, suddenly not at all embarrassed to ask the question.

"Of course. She would cater to my every need, be attuned to my every whim."

"Oh, I see," she said with a slow drawl. "You want what women want from their men!" she exclaimed, as if understanding for the first time. "Why didn't you say so?"

Suddenly he was the wary one. "What do you mean? What are women looking for?"

"Well, a woman wants a man who can sense her moods, who can second-guess her wants before she has to state them. They want someone romantic, not necessarily sexy or macho."

"What's the difference between romantic and sexy?" He shifted his position, sitting on the couch and placing her head in his lap, lazily stroking her hair back from her face. He leaned his head back and his voice sounded slow and hazy, as if he were totally relaxed.

"Romantic is sending flowers, macho is thinking that delivering yourself for a night of action is the grand prize for some lucky girl. Romance is stroking my forehead, like you're doing right now. Sexy is grabbing my arms and punishing me with kisses." She knew that wasn't much of a description, but it was the best she could come up with for something that was more feeling than doing.

He chuckled. "It sounds as if romance wouldn't get you very far, while the other would turn into a wrestling match."

"Yes, but women like romance," she persisted, her hand finding his and pulling it over to caress the line of her face.

"And men like sex."

"So do women, eventually," she finally admitted to the darkened room. If he happened to hear, well, that was all right, too.

The door was pushed open, spilling a bright trail of light into the room. Cara attempted to sit up, but J.T. kept hold of her shoulders. "How's it going, Sam?" he said calmly.

"Jus' fine," Sam drawled, squinting to see them before his eyes widened in surprise. "I was just wonderin' where Caro had disappeared to. Thought I'd better check."

"She's fine. We're just relaxing," J.T. assured him. "If it's all right with you, I'm going to take her home in a few minutes. She'll be back in the morning to do the books and ordering. Tonight I think she ought to get some sleep," he explained. "You need me to do anything before I leave?"

"Naw, just take her home and let her rest. Everything's under control. It's a good idea, her working in the morning. More civilized," he mused, as if he had thought of it himself.

"Thanks, Sam," she murmured, relaxing back in Joseph's lap with a soft contented sigh. "See you early tomorrow."

"Right," the old cowboy chuckled as he closed the door. Somehow he didn't think she'd be up as bright and early as she thought she'd be.

By the time J.T. got her home and into bed and followed suit himself, she was totally out for the count. He stared down at her.

That night he had gotten closer to her than he ever had before. Did that mean that she was lowering those almost impregnable defenses? Would he ever be able to get through to her and show her just how much he was beginning to care? He was afraid of the word "love." Hadn't he seen too many other men fall under love's spell only to find a day, a week, a month, or a year later that it had been fool's gold, bright and shiny for the moment, but not worth anything when the time came to count on it.

But his feeling for Caro was something very special. He hesitated to label it just yet. Fear of rejection was just one of his reasons not to paste a name on the flow of emotions he felt when he saw her. But soon, soon . . .

He lifted the sheets and slid between them, his leg coming into electric contact with hers. The mother of his child. Would she really be that? He hoped not yet. If he had been smart he would never have taken her to bed in the first place! He would have stayed with his original plan and taught her the lesson he had had in mind instead of teaching her how to make love so very well. . . .

For Caro, the pattern of the days was set. In the morning she would fuss over a big breakfast. J.T. would humor her, eating and talking during their time together. Then he would leave for Salt Lake City and she would dress in jeans and a shirt and go to the club to order supplies and do the books. By late afternoon she was home, and by early evening J.T. was back. They would spend a leisurely evening in together, talking, munching, sipping light wine. There was never an awkward moment from the time he walked in until the time they went to bed. Some nights they made passionate love and other nights he would touch her as if she were something precious that would fall apart with rougher handling. And occasionally he just held her in his arms, his mouth teasing her temple with a kiss as a sigh of contentment passed his lips. It was a time of absolute magic and Caro didn't think any further ahead than the next day, willing herself to ignore the future.

When the telephone rang just before J.T. was due to arrive one day, Caro thought nothing of it. No chill of premonition stirred her.

"Hello?"

"Hello, is Mr. Joseph Cole there?" a small wavering voice asked.

"No, he's not. May I take a message?" Alarms sounded in her head. No one had ever called J.T. except his secretary. No one. Then a second thought came on the heels of the first. Cole? J.T. was related to Brandon Cole! His last name wasn't Thomas, as she had thought. She gripped the receiver tightly, her knuckles whitening.

"Will he be there later?" the woman asked. "I need to reach him immediately. Are you one of his secretaries?"

Caro took a deep breath. "He should be here shortly. May I have him call you?"

"Please. Tell him his mother called. I need Joseph home as soon as possible." The woman hesitated for a moment. "I don't want to alarm him, but his father isn't well. You will tell him, won't you?"

"Yes, yes, of course I will," she muttered into the

mouthpiece. "By the way, how is Brandon?" She threw the bait out almost in the hopes that it wouldn't be grabbed.

But it was. "Fine," the older woman said absently before homing in on her immediate problem. "I know how Joseph worries about the family, and he's needed here right now. I'm sure he'll understand that business will have to wait for a little while."

"I'm sure he will," Caro repeated in a monotone, thinking about the recent weeks when she had tried to coax him into staying home from work to be with her. He had been tempted, but not strongly enough to remain with her. But for his family she bet he would drop everything. Everything—including her.

Once more blood had proved to be thicker than water.

She replaced the receiver and walked over to the window to stare sightlessly out at the mountains.

Brandon's brother. Why hadn't she guessed? She had been so blind. He had entered into this strange setup in order to protect his own flesh and blood from her clutches. Reason made her accept the fact that he had stayed because of an attraction to her. She wasn't *that* blind. But she *had* been used.

Caro knew that she was being unrealistic in wanting him to refuse to go to his mother's side. It would make no sense for him to refuse to go to his father when he was ill. But as unreasonable as it sounded, she also knew that it would be just the first step in locking her out of his life. She still took second place. All the old, childish, hurting feelings were there again, showing themselves in self-pity and anguish. She thought she had outgrown those emotions, but the fact was that she was so jealous she could hardly control the pain that flooded through her.

Over the years Caro had searched out all the things that she had once been convinced were for others and not for her. She had found the roots she'd wanted, right there in Park City. She had found the beginnings of a family in Sam. Why couldn't she be happy with that? Why did she feel the need to have everything? Wasn't the fact that she knew she was carrying Joseph's baby enough? Did she have to try to hold on to Joseph, too? He had obviously followed her in order to get Brandon off the hook and not to claim her for his own. Besides, what if he did like her? In the end, wouldn't he grow to hate her for trying to hold him to something that had been just a fling for him? In fact, wouldn't it be better to end it now, before he ended it for her? Later might be too late to sever the emotional strands he was so good at weaving around her heart. Later she might hurt too much and bury her pride to try to keep him, perhaps even use the baby as a weapon. After all, love was one of the messiest of emotions, wasn't it?

She wiped away the hot tears that were suddenly cascading down her cheeks. It was time she faced the fact that she'd been living in a dream world and putting off the inevitable.

It was time to break away from J.T. Cole.

7

J.T. stood just inside the living room doorway, hands splayed on his hips, his stance one of aggression.

"What the hell do you mean, you want to end this before it turns into a relationship! What in the world do you think it is now?"

Her voice and face were calm, almost devoid of any emotion. "I think it could be the beginning of something that I don't want to get into. I also believe that this is the perfect time to end it. Your parents need you and I now know I'm not pregnant."

His eyes narrowed on her. "How do you know?"

"The usual way a woman knows whether she's pregnant or not," Caro lied. "Besides, I've decided to give up the idea. I'm too old and too settled to have a child upsetting my routine. It was just a dream, that's all, one that came too late in life."

"You didn't seem to think you were too old to

have a baby four weeks ago." His voice held an accusatory tone.

"I hadn't thought it out all the way through," she explained. "Now I have."

"And now you want me to quietly pack my bags and never darken your door again?"

"Yes."

"After everything we've done and felt for each other?"

"Yes."

He raked an impatient hand through his hair. His air of confused puzzlement was an agony to watch, making her far more vulnerable than she could cope with for much longer. She turned and stared out the window with tear-blurred eyes. Couldn't he see that she was doing this as much for his good as hers? He would never be happy in an arrangement like this. He was the product of a family and she was giving him back to them as much as she was freeing herself from dreams without substance. "Don't make this any harder than it already is, J.T.," she pleaded.

"I see. Just leave quietly and without any fuss or muss. Good-bye, it's been fun." His voice was bitter.

Suddenly his hands clamped down on her shoulders, spinning her around to face his anger and frustration. "Damn it, Caro! This doesn't make sense! We have something special going with each other! We shouldn't leave it now."

"What do we have, J.T.? Sex? Love?" she asked, her eyes searching his face, as if the answer were written there. "Do you love me or do you love to make love to me? Which is it?"

The room rang with his silence as he struggled to put his answer into words. "I know I love to make love to you. You know that, too. It's not something that's easy to hide. I feel warm, protective, and loving toward you. If that's what you think love is, then I love you. I haven't had a chance to stop and analyze my feelings at this point."

She refused to allow her face to show the searing pain she felt at his words. If he didn't love her now, then he certainly wouldn't suddenly fall in love with her next week or the week after, or even in six months, when she would look bulky and swollen with his child. . . .

"In that case, you should leave now, before we become any more involved with each other. Later on our relationship might become a habit and it would be even harder for us to part, even though that's probably what we'd have to do eventually," she countered. "You know we have very little in common, certainly not enough to base a long-term relationship on."

"And do you want a long-term relationship, Caro?" His voice softened as he watched the play of emotions across her face. She could camouflage a lot, but not everything.

Anger was her only recourse. She had to hide behind something or he would discover the strength of her already battered emotions. "No. I don't want *any* relationship! I tried from the beginning to find a surrogate father—not to have an affair! You're the one who walked in here and switched around the terms! This was never supposed to be, don't you see?" she argued. "I want you to leave now. I promise I won't try to contact your family or reestablish any business dealings with your brother. I just want my life back the way it was!"

His eyes widened in understanding when she mentioned his brother. "You're angry because I didn't tell you my name or my relationship with Brandon, aren't you?"

"I was irritated about that, yes," she admitted. "But it wasn't the end of the world."

"I didn't realize that you would take Thomas for my last name at first," he explained. "But when you did, I let it slide. I was going to tell you as soon as I thought you could cope with it."

"I'm coping with it now. I just want you to leave so I won't have to cope with that or anything else you may or may not have told me. I don't want you here, don't you see?"

"You're frightened of how close we've become," he murmured softly, believing that he finally understood.

"No. You obviously think there's something deeper in our relationship than I do. I feel nothing but an immense irritation at the way you've upset my life! Now go call your mother; she has something to say to you."

Her words were like a slap in his face. His hands tightened convulsively on her shoulders as he stared at her unbelievingly.

"My God, you mean it!" His breath came out in a whoosh, fanning her neck and shoulder and sending chills down her spine. His look of understanding turned to incredulity and then, finally, to disgust. "Well, perhaps it was just too late to save you from being a dried-up old spinster. You've cut yourself off from people for so long, Caro, that you can't respond to them with honest emotions anymore. I bow in defeat to you. Your wall is too high for me to scale." His hands dropped to his sides and he turned to walk back to the hallway before finishing his statement. "Besides, I'm not sure that the effort would be worth the prize," he said coldly as he looked her up and down. "I'll be packed and gone in an hour."

Caro sat in the darkened living room until long past midnight. The tears that she had thought would have been dried up by then continued to fall. She would get herself under control for just a few moments, and then they would come again.

She had watched him take his suitcases to the car, her heart beating erratically as she thought of a thousand different ways to keep him there. All of them meant that she would have to say the three words she never wanted him to hear from her: I love you. And it was true. If she hadn't realized it before, it was a certainty that she knew it then.

And love never did anything but hurt.

Love would force J.T. to make a choice between his family and her every time they had an argument. It would mean that if he ever chose his family over her she would have no one to lean on, to help her, to bolster her the way he did. Once again she'd be left out.

She straightened her shoulders and blew her nose in her already sodden handkerchief. But not anymore. Soon she'd have a child of her own to care for and to love. And until then, she'd just have to remember how it had been before J.T. Cole came on the scene and try to live that way again.

She could do it. She *would* do it. But that night she'd sleep on the couch rather than in the bed that she and J.T. had shared.

In the days that followed, an aching loneliness was always with Caro, but it was especially bad in the early evening, when she sat down at the dinner table by herself. At those times she would remember how J.T.'s eyes would light on her when he came through the door after work. She'd remember the times when she had to slap his hands away from the freshly peeled vegetables or order him into an apron to help open a can of something or other. He never could master the can opener. Every time he used it he would either splatter the liquid over himself or all over the counter. He had always set the table, carelessly spreading forks and knives in the center and napkins directly on the plates. He had explained just how he and his brothers had helped his mother at mealtime and how she, too, had given up hope of her men being able to learn the finer points of etiquette. After remembering night after night, Caro finally gave up and began taking her plate into the living room, sitting in front of the TV to help focus her attention on something, anything, besides him.

But the worst was yet to come. Her bedroom was sterile, empty, without J.T. Every night she tossed and turned, unable to escape him even in her dreams. He was everywhere. Only when she dreamed that he held her in his arms did she give a ragged sigh and sleep contentedly.

She counted the days that had passed since he'd pulled out of the driveway and out of her life. Four. Five. Six. Seven. See, she could make it! she told herself. On the evening of the seventh day she celebrated her hard-won freedom by sipping a glass of wine as she watched the late afternoon sunset drape across the mountains surrounding the small skiing town.

When the phone rang she answered it tiredly but without qualms, priding herself on the control she'd acquired over her recently shaken emotions.

"Hello."

"All right, Caro. I give up." J.T.'s voice was as tired as hers had been, only his was also laced with irritation. "The only way we're going to get any sleep is if we get married."

Her hand gripped the receiver. "Oh? And who says I'm not sleeping well?" Her tone was sharp and just as irritated as his.

"I do," he answered in a no-nonsense voice. "I've passed your house late at night and seen the lights blazing like a beacon. If you're holding out for marriage, I'm willing."

Pain froze her throat, then seared her anguished nerves. "I'm not holding out for marriage, J.T. I never was. All I wanted was a baby, and I've even changed my mind about that." Had she ever. Now she needed his baby just to keep her link with the world and avoid going into a total depression.

The line was silent for a moment; then J.T. spoke

again, sounding hesitant, as if he were feeling his way. "Caro, what if I want the marriage? What if I've decided that I need that type of commitment?" He knew immediately that his words had been ill-chosen. "Don't you think we *both* need it?" He tried to soothe troubled waters, but he realized with a sinking feeling in the pit of his stomach that there was no way of retracting his words. What he needed had nothing to do with trying to convince her of what she needed.

"Do me a favor, Mr. Cole, and don't call again." Her voice was stiff with outrage, hurt, and an emotion she refused to put a name to. "I've only made a few mistakes in my life, and you were one of the biggest. Rest assured that I won't bother you or your family, and I expect the same courtesy from you. You've outstayed your welcome and I'd appreciate it if you would disappear—forever!" She slammed the phone down just in time, as the sobs worked their way out through her pain-ridden throat. She slid to the floor, wrapping her arms around her legs and allowing her head to rest on her knees.

He undoubtedly thought she had set out to trap him, seal him to her with his child as the adhesive! How conniving, how cunning, he must think she was! And how rotten *he* was for thinking such a thing! Her mind buzzed with thoughts and accusations, but everything came back to the same thing: She loved him with all her body and soul. And though he didn't love her, he desired her enough to marry her. A wry smile passed quickly over her lips. He wouldn't even want her after watching her grow fat with pregnancy. And he certainly wouldn't learn to love her if he found out that she had kept his child a secret from him! Any feelings he had for her would turn to pure and simple hatred if he ever learned the truth. She remembered the look of disgust on his face the night he had left. He had been so harsh and cold, but that would be nothing compared with the way he would look if he found out that she had deceived him.

He might even go to court and attempt to take the child away from her! No, no matter how much she loved him, they must never meet again. No matter how cruel she was to him on the phone, it was the best medicine for them both. Her hand gently rubbed her still flat stomach. It was best for all three of them.

Dr. Patterson was a real gem. She smiled broadly at Caro and leaned back comfortably in the big leather chair. "You're six weeks pregnant, Caro," she said, "and I bet you're already as pleased about this baby as I'm pleased for you."

Caro chuckled, the first excitement she had felt all week glowing in her unusually pale face. "Of course. Now I need to know what foods I should be eating, how much milk I should drink, how often I should see you, whether I should continue my walks . . . oh, so many things!"

"Hold it, hold it." The tall older woman laughed. "We'll get into all of that, but first we have some papers to fill out and I need to know how you want this child brought into the world."

"What do you mean?"

"I mean that you have several alternatives to choose from as far as the birth of your child is concerned." The doctor smiled. "You can have it in the hospital with a local anesthetic or a general anesthetic, or you can have natural childbirth. Which would you prefer?"

"Natural childbirth," Caro said unhesitatingly. "I may never have another child. I don't want to miss a thing!"

The doctor chuckled as she began scribbling on the chart. "Somehow I knew you'd say that. I'll turn your name and due date over to Brenda Settles and she'll contact you at the proper time about Lamaze classes. You'll start those when you reach your seventh month. But right now we'll just concern ourselves with getting you to April 3rd in good health."

They talked for a few more minutes, Caro paying strict attention to everything the doctor explained. Her lethargy of the past week lifted for a while, enabling her to see that, although J.T. and her brief glimpse of another kind of life had vanished, she still had a very precious memento to care for. And in time her empty, aching feeling would vanish. It had to, she told herself in quiet desperation. It had to.

The next five months were slow to pass. Caro continued to work hard getting ready to open the new club in Snowhawk on New Year's Eve. Her preoccupation with the club and its workings was only a shield, however, against the loneliness that still invaded her thoughts whenever she remembered J.T. She wouldn't have traded that time with him for the whole world, but the ache that it had left in her heart was sometimes almost too much to bear. She loved him totally, completely. And the life that stirred inside reminded her of that love with every passing day.

But she had been right to end that relationship. Better then, when the ties could be severed without squabbling over the baby or his family ties or his career versus her career, all the things that could destroy a marriage or any relationship. After all, if she missed him this much now, imagine how much it would have hurt if they had lost that love later, had perhaps even stayed together only to destroy each other, as she had seen happen in so many marriages. Or worse, what if they had remained together only to become immune to each other's emotional needs? That was what she told herself late at night as she unconsciously listened for J.T.'s footsteps on the stairs. That was what she thought when she sat down to a lonely cup of morning coffee and one boiled egg. And she was relieved that he wasn't there when she disrobed to take her shower and could see the outline of her now-protruding stomach in the mirror. She was at once proud and embarrassed. It certainly wasn't the sexy, svelte look that she hoped he remembered her for!

A glorious fall turned into an early, freezing winter, just what a ski resort needed. Caro went from work to home and from home to work with precise regularity. She ate by the clock, slept by the clock, and took her multivitamins by the clock. This baby, her baby, would have all the advantages she could give it.

As usual, Monday meant that she had to clean the house in the morning, then eat a lunch of broiled fillet of sole, half a bowl of rice and a green salad. Then it was down to the office to complete the books for the previous week before taking inventory for the coming week.

The front door of The Loose Noose squeaked when she walked in. Caro tried it again, checking to see which hinge was making the racket. Nothing should interfere with the customer and his pleasure.

"Sam?" she called, continuing to check the hinges. "Get me the can of oil, will you?"

She could hear his footsteps echo through the club as he grumbled his way to the back storeroom.

"I swear, Caro, you could find something wrong in a brand-new house. We'd have gotten to the door in the monthly repair check-up. It didn't have to be done this very minute," he complained good-naturedly as he bent to squirt the oil into the offending hinge. "I wish you'd pay more attention to your own life so's you'd leave my work load alone."

"Think of it this way, Sam," she teased. "If I did things your way you'd have nothing to gripe about and then you'd be bored to death!"

"The hell you say!" he muttered as they walked into the office. He sat down in his accustomed place and waited for her to do the same. "With that little babe you're carrying, I'd say we'd have our hands full anyhow." Suddenly his good mood was gone and concern showed on his face. "And if that man learns how you lied to him, I guarantee there'll be hell to pay. He has a right to know his child as much as you do, Caro, and you know it!''

Her face lost its teasing look and turned to stubbornly etched stone. "The baby is mine, Sam. No one else's. And J.T. won't find out unless you decide to tell him." She demanded that he answer the challenge.

"You know I won't, but that doesn't mean I approve of this whole mess. That man loved you and you took advantage of him." He could be just as stubborn as she was.

They had covered this ground before. Patience laced her tone as she answered. "I told you long ago that I wanted a child. The only exception was that we weren't going to get to really know the father. Now that you've met him, you've decided that he loved me and wants this child. Don't you think you're assuming a lot? He's not like you, you know." Her voice softened as she saw the hurt look that quickly crossed his face.

"I wouldn't let anyone hurt you, you know that," he stated quietly and she nodded her head in acquiescence before he continued. "But I know a man in love, Caro. And I also know what that special light in a man's eyes means, and yours too, for that matter. You had something mighty nice going, but you got frightened enough to run away from it."

"Perhaps," she finally admitted aloud. "But he's gone now. And if he had been so in love with me he wouldn't have left at all, Sam." She didn't realize just how wistful her voice sounded. "He would have stayed and overcome my objections."

Sam nodded. "Loving you made him vulnerable, missy, and he didn't have a choice. His pride was hit pretty hard." He leaned forward in his chair and captured her unhappy eyes with his own older and wiser ones. "Why don't you at least give him a chance?"

"No. When you know you'll be on the losing end of a fight, Sam, you don't fight. You run and hide until it's over." She smiled a sad, lonely smile. "Besides, I have the baby."

"Humph," Sam said, standing up and walking to the door. He placed his hand on the doorknob but didn't open it immediately. "It's a mighty lonely existence without love, girl. You need a man like flowers need rain. You're just too dad-gummed stubborn to admit it!" He left the office after having the last word.

Was he right? Yes, damn him! He was! She wanted that ache that could only be filled by J.T. to go away, but she knew that was an impossibility.

"Damn it, Mike! If you can't get this contract right, then let me know and I'll hire someone else to write it up!" J.T. exclaimed as he threw a sheaf of papers down on his already cluttered desk. He glared at his friend and attorney from across the wide expanse of desk between them. He had called Mike to his office as an attorney, but they both knew he was taking out his anger toward Caro as only one friend could to another.

"I can only get it right, J.T., if you give me all the terms you and this customer discussed. But adding them after the fact isn't helping either one of us."

Mike stood, containing the anger he felt toward his friend. J.T. hadn't been himself since he'd left Caro's side, but that didn't mean that he could take out his frustrations on everyone around him! "Write me a memo on the changes you're requesting and I'll get right on it," he snapped. "Otherwise you can take it up with another lawyer. Let me know." He began to walk stiffly away.

"Mike!" J.T.'s voice rang out, stopping the man in midstride. A sheepish look covered J.T.'s face. Where did he get off handing a tirade like that to a friend? "You're right, it was my fault for not giving you the correct information."

Mike grinned. That was the nearest he had ever heard J.T. come to apologizing. J.T. seemed to read his mind, because he smiled sheepishly.

"I also owe you another apology," J.T. said, stacking the papers in a more orderly fashion. "I owe you one concerning Caro. I said she was a lot of things she isn't and you tried to correct my initial opinion. I wasn't listening."

"Are you now?" Mike prodded.

J.T. nodded.

"Then why don't you go back and see her?"

"No. She made it perfectly clear that she doesn't want to see me again." His voice was harsh and uncompromising.

"Are you sure the lady wasn't protesting too much?" Mike sat down again, perching on the edge of the chair as he watched J.T. stand up to pace the length of the room. "Did you tell her that you loved her?"

"No! My God, if she knew that she'd really have

laughed me out of the house! As it was I barely got away with my dignity intact." It was the first time he had admitted just how deeply he had been hurt that afternoon. He closed his eyes in painful remembrance. Her face had been so pale, her eyes such a deep smoky brown. Her firm, slim body had been rigidly tense. But the telephone call later had killed any thoughts he might have had of storming her defenses. She had made it as plain as she could that she wanted nothing to do with him—ever. Not even a proposal had been able to soften her opinion of him. A thought suddenly came to him and he shot a narrowed look at Mike. "She hasn't tried to sign anyone else up for that crazy scheme of hers, has she?"

The young attorney hid his smile with effort. Jealousy stuck out a mile on J.T. If only they weren't both so damn stubborn! "No. She told me to cancel any interviews or plans for that project. She did say something odd, though," Mike remembered with a puzzled expression. "She wanted to verify that you had signed the contract. I said yes, and that I had a copy in her file, ready for her to pick up. She just said 'Good,' and that she would get in touch with me later."

J.T.'s stomach lurched. He'd kept on hoping that something would happen, that he would walk into a restaurant or a store, or down the street, and see her, looking in a department store window or sitting alone at a table. He had imagined their meeting hundreds of times. They would stop and talk and she would remember with a smile just how foolish she had been. And he would recall all the times he had almost called but hadn't. And they would laugh and pick up the pieces from that point. He would take her to bed and hold her in his arms, feel the richness of her skin again, lose himself inside the moist silkiness of her. . . .

The buzzer sounded and brought J.T. out of his reverie. "Yes, Sara?" he said to his secretary.

"There's a woman on line two who says she's calling to remind you about a class you signed up for last summer. Her name is Brenda Settles. Should I have her call back later?"

J.T. stood completely still. "I'll take it, Sara," he confirmed before punching the hold button. "Mike, don't leave," he ordered as the other man rose from his chair. "As my attorney, I want you to hear this conversation."

He punched another button, allowing the conversation to fill the room. "Hello, Brenda. How are you?"

"I was worried that you might not remember me, J.T." Brenda giggled.

"Oh, I always remember small brunettes with husbands named Ken and girlfriends named Caro," he teased, and only Mike knew that he wasn't in a lighthearted mood. "How are you doing and how are your classes going?"

"Well, that's what I'm calling about. I haven't seen Caro since shortly after I met you, but I did receive a call from her physician telling me that she's ready to attend the childbirth classes. I'm just checking to see if you're attending." She hesitated, hearing the silence at the other end. "She has to have someone act as a coach and, well, you did say that you wanted to be with her. . . ."

"Excuse me, Brenda, if I sound a little startled. I just returned from a business trip and haven't shifted mental gears yet. I didn't realize that Caro was far enough along to join the classes yet." The lie slipped off his tongue easily. How far into the pregnancy did she have to be before taking the classes? Five months? Six months?

Brenda twittered again. "I know you men. You think time's passing quickly until you see us going into these last few months. Well, Caro really is seven months along now, according to her doctor, so she's right on time for her classes."

J.T. stared at Mike, who colored under his scrutiny, giving his shoulders a jerk that meant he knew nothing about it. "I see." J.T.'s mind spun quickly with the new information, sifting the alternatives. "I'll be there, Brenda. Give me the date and time." He quickly scribbled the address and date on a pad, along with Brenda's number. "And by the way, Brenda, thanks for calling." He hung up the phone and once more faced his friend and lawyer.

"Can I sue her for custody despite the contract, Mike?" he asked quietly, the silent rage inside him contained for the moment.

"I can't advise you, J.T., you know that. I'm also Caro's attorney," the now-perspiring lawyer hedged.

"Damn it! You're my friend! *Can I sue her for custody?*"

"Yes!"

The steam of J.T.'s building emotions was expelled when he heard that single word. A small smile played at the corners of his mouth. It wasn't pleasant—it was triumphant. "Thanks," was all he said.

8

Four couples sat in the upright wooden chairs that were grouped in a corner of the room, and all of them seemed to be as excited and nervous as Caro was.

Brenda stood to one side, waiting for everyone to settle down. She focused on Caro and gave a solemn wink. Caro grinned back, then guided a reluctant Sam to two empty chairs on the side of the room. She reached into the depths of her oversized purse for a pen and pad. Tonight was to be orientation. Caro would be told what to bring and what to expect at all the future meetings. She just hoped that Brenda wouldn't ask where J.T. was. His absence was conspicuous, especially since Sam was so obviously uncomfortable in these surroundings. Sam had agreed to come to the first few sessions, but had adamantly refused to actually be her coach. He had agreed only to be a stand-in until she could find someone else who could fulfill that function. Sam could be relied upon to help her in any way . . . except with the actual delivery. She would have to find someone else, perhaps even Brenda, to be in the delivery room when her time came. Right now Sam was just moral support.

The only thing she was sure of was that this was the method she really wanted to follow to have her baby. Anything less would mean missing out on an experience she would have only once in her lifetime.

Brenda caught her eye and grinned as she made a circle with her forefinger and thumb. Caro smiled in return, trying not to show her puzzlement. What did that mean? Obviously Brenda thought everything was fine.

"All right, prospective parents," Brenda said to gain everyone's attention as she glanced at her watch and then at the door. "We'll begin now, because there's so much to cover tonight. I'd like to start by having everyone give their name and tell what they expect from this class and why they chose this method of giving birth. Donna, will you start off for us?"

Donna, a pert young ash blond who looked farther along than the required seven months, began talking, glancing at her equally young husband every now and then. Her husband, introduced as Bob, was obviously a construction worker, for he held a shiny yellow hardhat, which he nervously twisted around in his large hands. Caro sat back, relaxing as she realized that they were all interested in the same thing, giving a healthy start to a happy baby.

As Donna finished and Bob gave his stumbling rendition of the same tune, all eyes swiveled to the door to focus on the newcomer standing at the entrance.

Caro hid her irritation at the interruption, her eyes never leaving Bob's face until he had stopped his explanation and looked toward the door, too.

"Come in, come in," Brenda called gaily to the visitor. "I didn't know if you were going to make it tonight or not."

It was with a sense of fatalism that Caro finally turned to see who the others were watching. Her face slowly turned a parchment white before she blushed at being caught red-handed, like a small child being found out in the act of doing something very, very wrong. J.T. stood watching her with narrowed eyes, his taut frame blocking the doorway as he patiently waited for her to acknowledge his presence. The look in his eyes was frightening. They were cold, a deadly, angry brown. His expression silently spoke of his knowledge of her deceit and his contempt for her. Her heartbeat quickened in response to the promise of danger and her throat dried up in anxiety.

"I'm sorry I'm late," he murmured to Brenda with a quick, pseudo-apologetic smile as he finally left the doorway and walked toward Caro. "You can go back to The Loose Noose, Sam. I'll handle it from here." J.T. spoke quietly but with absolute authority. Sam grinned, stood, and relinquished his chair with a look that spoke of his relief at being replaced.

He leaned down and gave Caro a light kiss on the

cheek. "You'll do fine. Don't worry," he whispered in her ear before slapping his worn hat against his thigh and walking out the door.

J.T. sat in Sam's chair and stared straight ahead, toward Brenda. Within seconds Bob began his speech again and everyone's attention was once more focused on him. Everyone's attention but Caro's.

Sam had deserted her! He had left her here to cope with J.T. on her own! She was frightened to death as a thousand confused thoughts sped through her mind. What was he feeling? How had he found out?

She sat with her hands clenched in her lap, hoping that the small nerve that jumped in her wrist wouldn't show. But it did. He let her know by placing his finger on the beat. To everyone else it looked like a gesture of love, but she understood better than they did. He was telling her that she deserved to be frightened. To Caro's further embarrassment, the baby chose that moment to give a healthy kick. J.T.'s arm was pushed only slightly, but it was enough for him to feel the miracle of it.

His eyes widened as he waited in awe for the next kick, which occurred almost immediately after the first. His hand left her fingers to rest on the spot in order to better feel the movement, his unguarded expression clearly showing the sense of wonder he felt. Caro stiffened at the intimate contact until she saw his face out of the corner of her eye. The depth of his emotions had brought a shine of tears to his eyes as he realized the first staggering reality of his child's movements. *His child!* He was totally spellbound with the thought of their creation. His hand shook slightly as he finally lifted it from her stomach. In exchange he took her hand in his and held it tightly, almost to the point of hurting her, as he made a giant effort to compose himself and listen to the others speak. Once or twice he cleared his throat and she realized just how hard he was working to keep his emotions in check.

Sam had been right. What had entitled her to hold the knowledge of his child from him? He had every right to be angry, ragingly angry, with her. He had done everything the way she'd asked him to. He had signed the release papers, kept out of her business. He had even helped her both physically and emotionally. All that he had asked was that the baby be conceived naturally and that he be allowed to stay until its birth. And she hadn't even had the courage to tell him she was pregnant! She glanced at him again, and this time her eyes were caught by his. They spoke volumes to each other without a word being said. Long-pent-up emotions and thoughts that had never been uttered flew between them. She knew then that he would be there for every class and she also knew that she would accept him back into her life. Neither one of them had a choice. They hadn't realized it at the time, but all the choices had disappeared into thin air when they first met, and only one path was open to them now.

Now they could only try to bridge the gap that time had made. Now she would try to bring him up to date on the growth of his child and he would tell her what slot he wanted to fill in her life. And she would agree, no matter what, because having him with her was the most completely right feeling she had ever experienced in her whole life. So what if his family called him back to their side later? So what if he left her for the closeness a lifetime had forged? She would have him with her now, for this moment in time, and would give him something he had never had before: a child.

"Pax?" she whispered.

"For now," he answered softly. "But you have a lot to answer for."

"Don't we all," she whispered in return.

When the meeting was over and sheaves of paper with instructions had been handed out along with other supplies, the couples began their slow migration toward the door, reluctant to leave behind the contact with others who were experiencing the same things. Caro waited for J.T. to finish his chat with Brenda, who had come over at the end of her speech to talk with him.

Caro could feel an unreasoning jealousy flood her whole being. She stood waiting, feeling clumsy and fat and awkward compared to Brenda, who was so tall and slim and graceful. Suddenly Brenda was the epitome of everything Caro had wanted to be as she was growing up. Was Brenda J.T.'s ideal, too? Caro knew he would never approach Brenda for an affair; his own morals were too strict for that. But what was his ideal woman like? Whatever it was, Caro was sure it wasn't what she had evolved into: a woman who thought of her business first and marriage last on a list of goals.

Her hands began to shake once more. She and J.T. would soon be home and he would demand an explanation. How could she possibly tell him that she had sent him away because she loved him and was terrified of losing him at some point when she was even less ready to live without him? How could he understand her intense yearning for something that had been unattainable for so long that by the time he came along she was actually fearful of having her dream come true? What if reality turned out not to be as perfect as she had imagined? How could she possibly tell him of her love for him? She couldn't. It was as simple as that.

"Ready?" Without waiting for an answer J.T. took her arm and ushered her to the door, waving good-bye to those who had lingered. He never loosened his grasp as they headed toward his car.

"I have my—" she began, but he interrupted.

"Leave it. We'll get it in the morning."

"But—"

"I said leave it." His patience was all but gone.

The five-minute drive back to Caro's house was the longest and quietest she had ever known.

When the car stopped and she reached for the handle, he got out and came around to her side, helping her out with a steadying grip as if she were a prisoner about to make a run for it. In fact, there was no such thought in her mind.

In a way Caro was glad that the time had come to confront him and get it over with. As a child she had always preferred a spanking to some of her foster mothers' idea of punishment: a restriction. Now she felt the same way. Once the confrontation was over she could continue with her life again.

She was sure she knew what he would say. He

wanted to marry her and bring up the child with a
father. He realized that although a contract had been
signed, it was worthless. No court would allow it to
stand. He had seen an article on a similar case just
the other day, and the father had been given full
rights. He would probably say that they could di-
vorce later if she wished, but the child would be
protected at all costs. He would never relinquish
what was his.

"The kitchen," he ordered. "I want some hot tea
with plenty of sugar." She obeyed wordlessly.

Before Caro could turn around J.T. was filling the
teakettle and setting it on the stove to boil.

"Let's get this over with, J.T.," she prodded in a
weary tone. "I'm exhausted and I want to get some
sleep." Suddenly a thought occurred to her, making
her heart thud with the depressing knowledge. She
had been betrayed. "Sam told you about the baby,
didn't he?"

"No. Sam never said a thing. The only news I
could glean from him was that you were healthy and
still in business." The air in the room crackled with
invisible electricity as he turned to shoot a look at
her. "Damn his tough old hide! I called him every
week and he never said a word about the baby!"

Her hands dangled helplessly by her sides. "Then
how . . . ?"

"Your friend Brenda had my card and was supposed to inform me the moment you were to begin
classes. Remember? Only she hadn't seen you in so
long she didn't know that we weren't together, let
alone that I had no knowledge of my own child."

"I don't work in the evenings anymore." Her chin

lifted, her brown eyes growing cold. "And how do you know it's yours?"

"Don't try to play games with the big boys, Caro. You're in the minor leagues. It's my child and you'll go through a series of tests to prove it if need be."

"All right. Now what?"

"Now I move back in, coach you in childbirth, remain until the baby is born, and see that everything is as it should be. Then I receive unlimited visitation rights. I won't put myself through the degradation of asking you again to marry me, only to be turned down by your viper's tongue. I learned my lesson the first time."

It took her a moment to absorb his words. Her anger dissolved, leaving unshed tears in its wake as she felt her spirits plummet. All her dreams of a knight on a white horse coming to rescue her from herself were shattered. She had grossly miscalculated. He didn't want her or the child. He just wanted to do what was right. Her own instincts had proved to be totally wrong in almost every respect. "I see," she muttered, as she stared out the kitchen window. Her self-esteem plummeted even further. He didn't want anything from *her*, he just wanted the right to his child later.

"I doubt that very much," he said dryly, a hint of exasperation in his tone. "But right now I want an explanation. Did you know you were pregnant when you asked me to leave?"

"Yes."

"Then why did you do it? Did you think I would abide by that damned contract?"

"Yes."

The teakettle whistle blew and he turned his back on her as he found the tea and the small porcelain teapot. Within seconds his tea was brewing and he was sitting down at the table as if he had lived there all his life.

He took a sip, lounged back in his chair, and stared at her. "What did you hope to gain by kicking me out of your life?"

"Peace," she answered instantly, realizing as she said it just how silly it was.

"Explain," he said curtly.

She began slowly, haltingly. "You upset my life. I've lived by myself too long to have someone else interfere with the running of it. You were telling me when to take my walk, what to eat, when to work, when to go to bed."

"Correction: when to make love. You could have gone to bed whenever you wanted."

"Whatever." She whisked the idea away with a wave of her hand. "Then you would go off in your car to slay dragons somewhere else, expecting me to be here when you returned."

"Correction two: *hoping* you'd be here when I returned. You did the expecting, Caro, by trying to live up to what you thought you should do. You expected me to act in a particular way and therefore imposed it upon me to do so. I didn't ask you to clean house or cook or take care of me. I wanted you to act naturally, normally, with me. If you had done those things because you wanted to, I would have loved it. More than anything I hoped you would behave that way because you wanted to . . . not because I asked you to. They weren't my expectations you were living up to—they were yours. You have some preconceived notion of what a family should be like, and you were determined to act out those notions of yours."

With a blinding flash of insight Caro knew he was right. She had always had a fantasy family that she would one day belong to, only her expectations had never been tested to prove them fact or fiction. "Perhaps I did," she admitted wearily. "What good does it do to rake it all up now?"

"Because now we're starting over. I'm moving back in tomorrow and I will remain here until after the baby is born." His eyes narrowed as her mouth formed the beginning of a protest. "You owe me that, Caro. I missed seven months of watching my child grow and develop. Seven months of being with you as a family. The kind of family that *we* would be, not something pulled out of books or movies."

"Most men wouldn't care to be around during morning sickness anyway," she tried to joke, a large lump in her throat getting in the way.

"I'm not most men." He nodded toward her stomach. "I'm the father of that child and I had a right to be here. You denied me that right."

"Fine! All right! You're here now!" she shouted. "Just don't expect to stay with me for a few days then run off to your family or another girlfriend and then expect me to allow you back in!" Her face paled. She hadn't meant to say that, no matter how long she had thought it.

A golden hue entered his dark eyes as comprehension dawned. "You were angry about my mother's phone call, is that it?"

"No!" she denied too quickly and far too loudly to be believed.

"I don't believe you. The night before her call we made love together, beautiful, natural love. The following morning you woke up in my arms and I knew you felt the same way I did. I knew it." He voiced his thoughts aloud, as if she weren't even in the same room. "Emotions that run as deep as ours aren't something you can hide—except in anger. When I left for work I had several stops to make along the way. It wasn't until late in the day that I found out my father was ill. And when I got home, you had changed. Drastically." He stared at her, his eyes searching to find the answers she had never allowed anyone to see.

With lithe grace J.T. stood and walked around the table, stopping to touch her swollen belly. "But the one thing that stands out in my mind was the fear that showed in your eyes. I'll never forget seeing that. I thought you were afraid of me. But it wasn't that, was it? It wasn't me you were afraid of. It was you. The one thing you wanted, a family, was within your reach, and you were suddenly terrified that it wouldn't live up to all your dreams and expectations. Better to reject it and be lonely the rest of your life than to have to live with the reality of it. I should have known."

"You're wrong," she denied hoarsely, stepping back. "You're very wrong."

"Then explain it to me, Caro. I'll listen. Explain to me how I can be so wrong. You cared for me. I know you did. All this time I thought I rushed you when I asked you to marry me, but that wasn't it. What was it? It couldn't have been the fact that I desired you so much, that I wanted to hold you constantly. You didn't seem to mind that as much as you do now."

She gave a short laugh, her eyes glued to the dark, curly hair peeping over the partially opened collar of his shirt. She couldn't bear to see what was in his eyes. "Oh, of course. I'm so desirable now that you can't wait to get your hands on me." Her voice was brittle, bitter. It was the first time she had regretted her pregnancy. She would have given anything for one lascivious look from him. She would have given anything but her baby.

His hands rose to rest on her slender shoulders. "Does it show that much?" he asked quietly.

Her startled eyes locked with his. Was he laughing at her? Playing with her already raw feelings?

No, his expression answered, he wanted her. Her heart swelled in her breast as she realized the depth of his desire for her. Slowly, cautiously, he enfolded her in the comfort of his arms, his cheek resting against hers as if it belonged there. She didn't realize that she had wrapped her arms around his waist until she felt the pressure of his buckle against her stomach. An intense feeling of contentment flooded through her to J.T. as she felt the ridged muscles of his back relax as if for the first time in a long time.

"I've missed you so much, Caro. So much," he whispered, his voice reflecting the deep sense of relief he felt now that the pain of missing her was gone. She knew just what he meant. Hadn't she felt the same way? Hadn't she hurt so terribly that she couldn't sleep nights or laugh during the long, lonely days? She had managed to exist since he had gone, but existing wasn't living.

The teapot sat forgotten on the table, cooling in the late evening air, as J.T. took a step away and stared down at her. They were on another plane of existence. He extended his hand toward her and she confidently placed hers in his. Her face shone with the knowledge of his intense desire for her.

Casually, slowly, as if they had all the time in the world, they turned and walked toward the stairs and up to the bedroom that they had, it seemed now, always shared.

The bedroom was dark. Light spilling in from the hallway gave just enough illumination for them to see the outlines of the furniture.

J.T. reached up and began unbuttoning his shirt with one hand, the other still holding hers. Suddenly she was frightened, embarrassed. Was he remembering her as she had been? Would he laugh at the rotund, comical figure she now presented? She hesitated, not wanting to expose herself to his ridicule.

"Tell me," he said softly, realizing that she was struggling with something.

"I don't want you to see me this way." The words were wrenched from her.

"You're more beautiful now than you ever were before. Why be shy?"

"I'm not like I was before. I'm clumsy and awkward and I don't think I'll light many fires looking like this." She tried to make a joke of it, but couldn't carry it off.

"I made you like this. Should I feel as if I hurt you? Made you ugly? Because I don't. I feel that in some indescribable way I helped to make you as beautiful as you are to me right now. Won't you let me take pride in what I helped to create?" His voice was gentle, teasing. His thumb rubbed against the palm of her hand in a sensuous, rhythmic motion.

Her movements were jerky and painful as she undressed in the dimness. It took every ounce of nerve she had to disrobe. She moved into the shadowed area of the room, where she hoped he couldn't see her.

Before she could slip between the sheets J.T. was with her, holding her close, touching her with the intimacy of his own body. He felt the indented line of her back, the smoothness of her shoulders, and the curve of her slim neck. His hands traced every contour, every nuance, before he filled them with her soft breasts. A sigh escaped him as he realized their tender fullness. When his hands left them they traveled downward until they were splayed across her stomach. She was mesmerized by his gentle contact with her. Nothing she had ever dreamed of had prepared her for his awe at the child they had created.

He slowly fell to one knee, his head resting on her belly as if he were listening for the child to speak. "Our child, Caro. A child that only you and I could have created together," he whispered in an emotion-charged voice.

Caro's hands rested lightly on his shoulders as she stared down at the top of his head. Tears flooded her eyes. She had tried to cheat J.T. of all the love he had to give. But what was worse, she had tried to cheat her child of its loving father.

His name was wrenched from her lips.

He stood, engulfing her in his arms once more before laying her down on the bed as if she were a piece of rare porcelain. He lay down beside her, his hands moving along a path they had taken before.

"J.T., I don't . . ." she began to say.

"Hush, darling," he crooned in a low, deep voice. "There are other ways. So many other ways." His assurance relaxed her and she melted against him, confident that he would lead her down the right path to their own personal delight.

He talked to her, held her, soothingly stroked her. He touched her body from cheek to instep, bringing all the small nerves that had lain dormant inside her vibrantly alive. Her blood hummed as his hands worked magic in ways she had never dreamed of before. They continued together up that fantasy hill until they reached the crest, holding their breath at the wonder of each other's touch. And then they gently floated back to earth, held comfortingly in each other's arms.

Then they slept as they had not been able to for months, deeply and without dreams.

9

᠅᠅᠅᠅᠅᠅᠅᠅

J.T. leaned back, relaxed against the headboard of the bed, his hand on Caro's abdomen as he felt the baby move around. "I knew we'd make a power-house of a baby," he said smugly. "I just didn't realize I was speaking in literal terms."

Caro chuckled, moving his hand with hers as the baby shifted its position. "It's your young blood," she teased. "I never should have taken a boy to my bed."

"Why not? I bet I've been taking one to mine for the past six weeks." His eyebrows wiggled up and down in an imitation of Groucho Marx and her chuckle turned into a full-fledged laugh. With his broken nose and heavy brows and cowlick, he was the epitome of a ragamuffin constantly in trouble.

"My poor child! I'd better start praying for a girl who looks like me. With your looks my son would always be defending himself . . . from other women."

"Our child," he corrected automatically, his head bending so his mouth could taste her exposed shoulder. "And I hope it's a girl who looks just like you, too. You'd make a pretty funny looking boy."

He worked his way around her shoulder to the base of her throat, placing a kiss at the small pulse point at the base. "Mmm. I'd better get out of here while I still remember that our sandbox days are over for a while."

"Or just beginning," she retorted before she realized what she had said. She quickly moved toward the side of the bed. That was something they had never spoken of: what would happen after the baby was born. They had both walked on eggs for the past six weeks, loving each other with abandon but making no commitments. It was the only dark spot in Caro's life, but it was a large one.

She felt as if they were living in a kind of limbo, where there was no future and no past, only the present. She dared not make plans for anything more advanced than the baby's coming because J.T. had mentioned nothing more than that. Oh, he would wonder what the child would look like at the age of one or two or ten or eighteen, but he never mentioned whether he would be seeing the child for any reason other than from a sense of duty. The days continued to roll past and Caro waited, worrying and wondering whether J.T. would be there later. The closer the time for her delivery got, the quieter she became. What could you talk about to a man you loved but didn't think would be there a week or so after your baby was born? It was true that, in the morning, when her mind was still fuzzy with dreams of what she wanted and not yet filled with the reality of what really was, they giggled and laughed and played like a couple of kids. But then he would go off to work and she would waddle downstairs to begin her day, and she would once more be reminded that he had never said that he wanted this arrangement to be permanent. And neither had she, a small voice answered, chiding her for her fears of being the first to say, "Stay. I want you to stay." Or, more important, "Marry me. Be my husband and father and best friend." What if he said no? It would be far more heartbreak than she could bear.

Every morning she thought about their tenuous relationship and every afternoon she pushed the thoughts back to ferment and grow in the darkened corners of her mind.

Despite the fact that she didn't know anything about J.T.'s plans after the baby's birth, he kept her constantly informed of his schedule all during this period before the great event. He called every time he left the office, went to lunch, or just wanted to chat. By the end of the day he had usually called at least twice, always asking the same thing. She grinned broadly when the phone rang. That day was no exception.

"Are you feeling all right? You're not climbing those stairs, are you?"

"Are you going to carry me upstairs when I get too big to walk?" she teased, her hand automatically rubbing her now huge stomach.

"No, I'll rent a crane to sit outside the house and

give the operator our spare bedroom so he'll be available day and night." His voice was light and teasing, wrapping her in the soft, warm glow of intimacy. This was how it would be if they were married.

"Sounds good to me. I suppose the expenses for this service are all yours?" she asked, a giggle in her voice.

"Mine? Not on your life! I pay for the crane, you pay the man. After all, you make plenty of money. And you're the one who's eating so much."

"I'm only eating this much because some do-gooder keeps asking me to lick my plate clean, telling me I'm eating for two."

"Remind me. I won't ask you to do that tonight. From now on, I'm a changed man," he retorted meaningfully, a strange emphasis on the last four words. "Tonight we're having a serious discussion, my Caro. So be ready." His warning sounded like a death knell to her ears and her lighthearted mood instantly disappeared. She instinctively knew that he was planning to announce his plans for leaving her. She also realized that she wouldn't be able to make it through the evening without breaking down. This was how relationships ended.

She quickly dialed Sam's number, but there was no answer. She tried the club, then the wholesaler's. Sam wasn't at either place. With each phone call she panicked just a little bit more. In the middle of dialing Brenda to ask her if she and Ken could come to dinner and delay the inevitable, the funny backache she'd had all morning suddenly got stronger. With the certainty born of a woman's deep-seated instinct, Caro knew that this was the baby's time.

Suddenly nothing else mattered and everything was all right! She gave a light-headed laugh. Now! Now was the time she'd been waiting for!

With calm deliberation she dialed the numbers they had kept posted near the phone for just this occasion. It took less than five minutes for her to get in touch with the doctor and the hospital. It took another five to call J.T. He, too, was calm and lucid—until he promised to be home in less than five minutes when they both knew he had a forty-mile drive through the mountains.

Her suitcase was in the hall closet, packed and ready. The car had more than enough gas to manage the three miles to the hospital and Caro had her keys and purse next to the phone. Everything was as it was supposed to be.

There wasn't time to think of anything but the next few hours. With careful deliberation Caro gathered everything and placed it by the front door, then sat down on the couch with her stopwatch, checking the time between contractions. They were six minutes apart. When they were five minutes apart it would be time to leave for the hospital.

Her baby was going to be born. Soon.

All her life she had dreaded being alone, yet she had forced herself to adopt that way of life so she wouldn't have to do the one thing she dreaded more: become vulnerable by loving someone else. Now her lonely life-style was over. She would soon have a baby on which to focus all her pent-up love.

She would survive. If J.T. left her, she would be devastated, but she would live because she would have a child to dote on and love. Her child. Their child. She'd make it.

Strangely enough, she finally saw the irony of her situation. Now that she was about to have someone else to love she knew that she could finally find the courage to speak to J.T. of her love for him. She could say the words that needed saying: Stay with me and be my husband.

How strange that it had taken a baby to show her how to be a woman.

The Alternative-Birth Center hospital room was decorated to look like a bedroom in a home. Pictures had been hung on the walls, the curtains matched the quilted bedspread, and the tile floor was covered with small shag rugs. The focus of attention, however, was the large double bed with the incubator and tray of instruments that stood beside it. Caro dropped her small carryall by the door and glanced around.

The kind and very young nurse watched with knowing eyes as Caro took a second look at the unfamiliar instruments that had been sterilized and wrapped in cellophane. "The bathroom is across the hall, Caro, and the kitchen is next door. If you decide you want a cold drink, there are some in the refrigerator." She moved to the closet. "Extra blankets and pillows are in here. So why don't you get undressed now? The doctor should be here any minute to examine you." She glanced down at the stopwatch around Caro's neck, her professional concern showing as she watched Caro time another contraction. "Are they speeding up?"

"Yes," Caro said breathlessly. "Three minutes apart."

"Oh, good!" The nurse praised her as if she had done something spectacular.

It took three minutes for Caro to slip out of her clothing and step into the shower, where she aimed the special vibrating spray toward her lower back. The pulsating water took the heaviness of the labor pains away, leaving only a deep, penetrating awareness of what would be happening in the coming hours.

Where was J.T.? Had something happened to him? Had he changed his mind? Perhaps he had realized at the last minute that he really didn't want to be present for the baby's birth. Some men didn't. . . .

Caro didn't move when the nurse knocked on the shower door. Her teeth clenched with a new contraction, despite the fact that she kept telling her body to relax.

"Is everything all right, Caro?" the nurse called.

"Yes," she muttered between her teeth. "Pain always affects me this way." Her breath hissed as she began to pant during the peak of the pain, just as Brenda had instructed her to do.

"Your doctor is here now and needs to examine you."

By the time Caro finished showering and slipped into her peach-colored shorty gown, her pains were even more intense, but she filed away any negative thoughts, focusing only on what was happening to her. Her heart kept floating up like a helium-filled balloon with the thought of the child to come. Soon she would have her own precious person to love. Soon.

Everything was going according to schedule—except that J.T. wasn't there. The doctor soothed her with her best professional bedside manner. The nurse, a twinkle in her eyes, hummed a tune off-key. And Caro exercised every breathing trick she had learned in the previous two months. At first she was surprised when they worked, but after the initial surprise wore off, she stopped thinking at all and simply concentrated on breathing the pain away.

When J.T. finally arrived Caro was able to smile for the first time since she had begun her journey. His hair was windblown and his suit jacket was gone, as was his tie. The top button of his pale cream shirt was undone and his sleeves were rolled up. But the look on his face was what warmed Caro the most. His concern was evident, his love apparent for all to see. His kiss was gentle, although his voice was as rough as sandpaper.

"If you'll have a seat behind Caro, Mr. Halter, as you were instructed in your classes, you can begin coaching her. She's very near delivery," the doctor prompted.

J.T. raised an inquiring brow at the doctor's use of Caro's surname, but all Caro could do was grimace, because another pain was making itself felt.

The next hour contained more emotion than Caro

had ever dreamed possible. Imagination and the films shown in the Lamaze class had been unable to explain the reality of the birth process.

J.T. was wonderful, helping her with her breathing and blowing techniques, slipping small ice cubes into her mouth to ease the dryness her breathing caused, rubbing the tenseness from her arms, shoulders, and back between pains, crooning to her words of encouragement that didn't matter as much as their tone. And when Caro neared the end of labor and they both could see the child of their making, her pride in their child couldn't be controlled.

"Fine, Caro, now push down one more time! That's it, that's it!" the doctor exclaimed. "You've got a beautiful baby girl, Caro," she said softly a moment later, holding the small, precious bundle up for them to see.

Caro collapsed against J.T.'s body, all her energy completely depleted. He cradled her in the comfort and security of his arms, watching with amazement over her shoulder as the doctor cleaned the small infant's eyes, nose, and mouth. Immediately afterward the baby was handed into Caro's outstretched arms and she cuddled the tiny, complete human being. The baby's wide blue eyes hazily attempted to focus on her mother's nose, to no avail. One small fist flailed the air before five tiny fingers wrapped around J.T.'s larger one.

"Caro, she's beautiful, just like her mother." His voice almost broke.

Both the doctor and Caro looked at him in surprise.

"Like her mother! J.T., Summer is the spitting image of her father!" Caro chuckled, glancing once more at the high cheekbones almost disguised by the baby's chipmunk cheeks and the full lower lip that quivered in hunger.

"And you've already decided on a name?" he asked softly, his eyes still glued to the small, perfectly formed baby in Caro's arms.

"It was the height of summer when she was conceived. It seemed a perfect choice. It was a perfect time."

His eyes locked with hers as the depth of her meaning became clear. They had been happy together, taking each day as it came without looking into the future and trying to dissect their relationship.

Suddenly he grinned. "As you say, a perfect choice for a perfect baby." His eyes lit up as he watched the mother of his child. Caro didn't see his possessive gaze as she carefully checked the baby over, making sure that all her fingers and toes were in the right places. Little Summer cooed, sneezed, howled, and became quiet, all in the space of a minute. If Caro had had the energy she would have laughed at the beautiful infant's innocent antics.

"Now, let's get the mother squared away and ready for her reward: plenty of rest," the doctor ordered. "J.T., you can stay with her if you want; that's one of the nicest features of our alternative birth plan. You did marvelously, Caro. Most women over thirty have longer deliveries." Her eyes twinkled with her next words. "Perhaps you were destined to have a whole brood of children!"

Caro moaned and the doctor chuckled. J.T. said nothing at all.

A short time later, Caro fell into a dreamless sleep, safely wrapped in J.T.'s protective arms.

Two days later Caro was able to go home. She was fine, Summer was fine, and J.T. was nervous. She knew that he was nervous because he wouldn't look her in the eye. Her heart dropped lower the closer they got to the house.

Now he was going to tell her that he had to leave. He would visit on weekends and see her later. It had been fun.

The nursery was ready for Summer, and Summer was asleep and ready for the nursery. Caro tucked the blanket tighter around the tiny miniature of her father and reluctantly left the room to join J.T. downstairs.

For once she was going to confront her problems head on and not run away or hide within herself as she usually did. She was going to force herself to ask him to stay and marry her. Summer needed him. And so did she. She knew that, just as she knew she loved him. She had no idea what his answer would be, but it would be better to hear him say no than to let him go and never know for sure what he would have said.

She followed the sound of banging pans, her curiosity aroused as she walked into the kitchen.

"Joseph?" she asked.

He was standing by the stove with every burner on. An apron was tied around his waist, a dishcloth was close at hand, and an endearing grin was plastered across his face.

"Sit down, the teapot's still hot. I'm cooking dinner," he said, stirring something in a small pot. "Tonight we're having my only specialty: pork chops in brown gravy with mashed potatoes and butternut squash."

"Dinner?" she repeated stupidly. She had expected him to tell her that he was leaving, not recite a menu!

He glanced over his shoulder at her before turning back to the stove and fiddling with the dials, apparently turning everything down to a simmer. "Will you sit down, Caro? You've just had a baby. Don't you know how to take care of yourself?"

Something in her snapped. "Yes, I can take care of myself, I always have! And my body tells me when I'm tired and when I want to sit! But right now I want to talk to you, damn it! Will you stop playing cook and bottle washer and sit down?"

He turned and stared at her, a small smile tugging at his lips. "Touchy, aren't we? Is this part of what they call postpartum depression?"

She ran a hand through her hair. "No."

"Then stop telling me to do what I just told you to do," he said with calm deliberation. "But, if it makes you feel better to see me sitting, I'll humor you." He took a seat, then waited for her to do the same.

Caro took a deep breath, sat down, and placed both hands on the table. She glanced up at him but lowered her eyes immediately when she realized that he was waiting for her to speak. Her nerves tensed and she faced the fact that she was a coward whenever she was with him. All her courage fled in his presence.

She forced herself to say the words, pushing them out breathlessly. "I appreciate all that you've done for Summer and me, and I want you to know that I appreciate it, but I want more from you."

His chocolate-brown eyes iced over. "Oh?"

The words she had been about to recite stuck in her throat. She could tell by his immediate reaction that he wasn't willing to love her and her baby, no matter how wonderful he had been. Her heart plummeted to her toes.

She waved one hand in the air, as if she could erase the words that had opened their conversation. "Never mind, it doesn't matter," she choked out.

"No, go ahead. What is it you want from me? Money? Child support? Palimony?" He spoke gruffly, contempt obvious in every word.

"No!" she exclaimed.

"Then what?"

"Never mind!" Anger forced her to stand, but she held on to the table top for stability. "I was going to tell you how much I love you and ask you if there was any way you could see yourself as part of our family, but Summer and I can do without you *and* your money! We don't need you! We don't need anybody!" Tears cascaded down her cheeks, but she didn't feel them. Her heart was breaking. She quickly turned to leave, wanting to hide in her room until he left—anything, so she wouldn't have to face him or her humiliation again.

"Caro! Wait!"

But she couldn't. She had to find a hiding place, so

she began to run out of the kitchen. Strong, slightly rough hands clamped down on her shoulders, stilling her flight.

"Let me go!" she cried, knowing that she would be unable to contain herself much longer.

"Caro, please," he muttered hoarsely, breathing in the scent of her hair as he buried his head in the crook of her neck. "Darling, stay." His hands stroked her arms, gentling her movements. "I accept your proposal of marriage."

She stilled immediately. "Don't tease me, Joseph," she begged.

"I'm not teasing. I love you, I have loved you, and I know that I'll always love you. And if you didn't realize soon that you loved me, I was going to march you down to court and demand that you marry me anyway." He took a deep, shuddering breath. "I was going to give you an ultimatum the night that Summer was born. I was going to tell you that you could marry me for love or you could marry me because of the baby. *But you were going to marry me.*"

She turned in his arms so she could face him, her bright brown eyes shining in wonder. "Really?"

He nodded. "Really."

Her heart sang. She could see his love in his eyes, feel it in the tender way his hands held her, as if she were a delicate flower that needed his loving care.

He smiled down at her, his hand coming up to touch her cheek gently. "When Brandon told me that you might hire him, and what for, I saw red. After I talked to Mike I was even angrier. I decided to teach you a lesson. I was going to string you along, act as if I was going along with your plan, then I was going to threaten you with a lawsuit for procuring males." He chuckled at her stricken look. "Don't look so worried, darling. It was only a pipedream. The minute I saw you I knew there was no hope, that I was only pretending anger. I fell for you immediately. I didn't stand a snowball's chance in hell of staying away from you. That's why I made sure you agreed that I could live here. I wanted, needed, to be near you."

She relaxed, teasing laughter lurking in the deep brown shadows of her eyes. "Oh, really? Then why did you keep your feelings such a secret?"

"Because, my dear, you were so busy trying to erect barriers between us that I was afraid to break down too many at once for fear of shattering you. I thought you might run away from me and then I wouldn't be able to get close to you again."

She wrapped her arms around his neck, looking at him through sooty lashes. "And then what happened?"

"Then I thought I could make you love the idea of my being here. I thought that if I became a fixture you'd let me stay. I didn't know then just how obstinate you are."

"I'm not being obstinate now," she murmured in a low voice.

J.T. leaned down and lifted her in his arms, carrying her down the hallway and into the living room. He sat her comfortably on his lap in the large wingback chair. Her head lay in the crook of his neck and shoulder, and she felt she was exactly where she should be.

"You frightened me, you know," she finally admitted.

"How?"

"You came from a large family and, from what you said, all of you seemed so close. I always wanted that but never had it. I think I was jealous."

He chuckled. "How anyone could be jealous of having a brother like Brandon is beyond me."

"But you seem so close to your parents," she insisted. "You were the first person your mother called when your father was ill."

"No, you just assumed that," he corrected. "But I am close to them. I can't help the sort of childhood you had, darling, but I can help make Summer's life better. She'll have aunts and uncles and cousins and grandparents. And she'll have us," he promised.

His lips softly caressed her forehead and she sighed with delight. Caro couldn't imagine a better place to be than in her own home, in J.T.'s arms, with Summer upstairs.

She finally broke the silence. "When?"

"When what?"

"When were you going to march me down to court?" she asked impishly.

"Tomorrow. As soon as I thought you were able. I was going to call my mother and have her come and take care of Summer, allowing her grandmother to get to know her. Then I was going to kidnap you and force you to marry me," he admitted unabashedly. "I already applied for the license and had the doctor do all the necessary blood tests when you were in the hospital." He grinned smugly.

"You *what?*"

He was unrepentant. "You heard me. She and I had a quiet discussion in the hallway after Summer was born. I explained that you were my wife in every sense of the word except one, and I wanted to remedy that. She understood and did the tests."

"I bet you also explained that you weren't Mr. Halter, too, didn't you?" she teased. A picture of his look when the doctor had called him Mr. Halter flashed through her mind, bringing a smile to her lips.

"You bet," he growled. "And there will be no 'Ms.' in this family. I want it perfectly understood that even though you have your separate business interests and I have mine, we are a team in everything else." He kissed the tip of her nose. "In the future I might even sell you on the idea of letting me take over the accounting for all your various interests."

"I don't know, I'd have to see what you have to offer." Her heart sang with the knowledge of his love.

"Plenty. Besides, you already owe me the eight thousand dollars I used to pay off Brandon and get him out of the state for a while."

Her eyes widened. "But, he didn't even—"

"—do his job?" he interrupted. "I know. I just didn't want him around while I did mine: making you see reason and know that I was the man you needed to hire. But make no mistake, Caro, our contract runs forever."

She snuggled closer to his chest, content in the warmth of his love.

And to think that she had almost given him up! And deprived Summer of this man who was her father!

Suddenly forever didn't seem nearly long enough.

This offer expires April 30, 1984.

Silhouette Desire
15-Day Trial Offer

A new romance series
that explores
contemporary relationships
in exciting detail

Six Silhouette Desire romances, free for 15 days!
We'll send you six new Silhouette Desire romances
to look over for 15 days, absolutely free! If you decide
not to keep the books, return them and owe nothing.

Six books a month, free home delivery. If you like
Silhouette Desire romances as much as we think you
will, keep them and return your payment with the
invoice. Then we will send you six new books every
month to preview, just as soon as they are published.
You pay only for the books you decide to keep, and
you never pay postage and handling.

YOU'LL BE SWEPT AWAY WITH SILHOUETTE DESIRE

$1.75 each

1 ☐ CORPORATE AFFAIR
James

2 ☐ LOVE'S SILVER WEB
Monet

3 ☐ WISE FOLLY
Clay

4 ☐ KISS AND TELL
Carey

5 ☐ WHEN LAST WE
LOVED
Baker

6 ☐ A FRENCHMAN'S KISS
Mallory

7 ☐ NOT EVEN FOR LOVE
St. Claire

8 ☐ MAKE NO PROMISES
Dee

9 ☐ MOMENT IN TIME
Simms

10 ☐ WHENEVER I LOVE
YOU Smith

$1.95 each

11 ☐ VELVET TOUCH
James

12 ☐ THE COWBOY AND
THE LADY Palmer

13 ☐ COME BACK, MY
LOVE Wallace

14 ☐ BLANKET OF STARS
Valley

15 ☐ SWEET BONDAGE
Vernon

16 ☐ DREAM COME TRUE
Major

17 ☐ OF PASSION BORN
Simms

18 ☐ SECOND HARVEST
Ross

19 ☐ LOVER IN PURSUIT
James

20 ☐ KING OF DIAMONDS
Allison

21 ☐ LOVE IN THE CHINA
SEA Baker

22 ☐ BITTERSWEET IN
BERN Durant

23 ☐ CONSTANT
STRANGER Sunshine

24 ☐ SHARED MOMENTS
Baxter

25 ☐ RENAISSANCE MAN
James

26 ☐ SEPTEMBER
MORNING Palmer

27 ☐ ON WINGS OF NIGHT
Conrad

28 ☐ PASSIONATE
JOURNEY Lovan

29 ☐ ENCHANTED DESERT
Michelle

30 ☐ PAST FORGETTING
Lind

31 ☐ RECKLESS PASSION
James

32 ☐ YESTERDAY'S
DREAMS Clay

33 ☐ PROMISE ME
TOMORROW Powers

34 ☐ SNOW SPIRIT
Milan

35 ☐ MEANT TO BE
Major

36 ☐ FIRES OF MEMORY
Summers

37 ☐ PRICE OF SURRENDER
James

38 ☐ SWEET SERENITY
Douglass

39 ☐ SHADOW OF
BETRAYAL Monet

40 ☐ GENTLE CONQUEST
Mallory

41 ☐ SEDUCTION BY
DESIGN St. Claire

42 ☐ ASK ME NO SECRETS
Stewart

43 ☐ A WILD, SWEET
MAGIC Simms

44 ☐ HEART OVER MIND
West

45 ☐ EXPERIMENT IN LOVE
Clay

46 ☐ HER GOLDEN EYES
Chance

47 ☐ SILVER PROMISES
Michelle

48 ☐ DREAM OF THE WEST
Powers

49 ☐ AFFAIR OF HONOR
James

Silhouette Desire

- 50 ☐ FRIENDS AND LOVERS Palmer
- 51 ☐ SHADOW OF THE MOUNTAIN Lind
- 52 ☐ EMBERS OF THE SUN Morgan
- 53 ☐ WINTER LADY Joyce
- 54 ☐ IF EVER YOU NEED ME Fulford
- 55 ☐ TO TAME THE HUNTER James
- 56 ☐ FLIP SIDE OF YESTERDAY Douglass
- 57 ☐ NO PLACE FOR A WOMAN Michelle
- 58 ☐ ONE NIGHT'S DECEPTION Mallory
- 59 ☐ TIME STANDS STILL Powers
- 60 ☐ BETWEEN THE LINES Dennis
- 61 ☐ ALL THE NIGHT LONG Simms
- 62 ☐ PASSIONATE SILENCE Monet
- 63 ☐ SHARE YOUR TOMORROWS Dee

- 64 ☐ SONATINA Milan
- 65 ☐ RECKLESS VENTURE Allison
- 66 ☐ THE FIERCE GENTLENESS Langtry
- 67 ☐ GAMEMASTER James
- 68 ☐ SHADOW OF YESTERDAY Browning
- 69 ☐ PASSION'S PORTRAIT Carey
- 70 ☐ DINNER FOR TWO Victor
- 71 ☐ MAN OF THE HOUSE Joyce
- 72 ☐ NOBODY'S BABY Hart
- 73 ☐ A KISS REMEMBERED St. Claire
- 74 ☐ BEYOND FANTASY Douglass
- 75 ☐ CHASE THE CLOUDS McKenna
- 76 ☐ STORMY SERENADE Michelle
- 77 ☐ SUMMER THUNDER Lowell
- 78 ☐ BLUEPRINT FOR RAPTURE Barber

- 79 ☐ SO SWEET A MADNESS Simms
- 80 ☐ FIRE AND ICE Palmer
- 81 ☐ OPENING BID Kennedy
- 82 ☐ SUMMER SONG Clay
- 83 ☐ HOME AT LAST Chance
- 84 ☐ IN A MOMENT'S TIME Powers
- 85 ☐ THE SILVER SNARE James
- 86 ☐ NATIVE SEASON Malek
- 87 ☐ RECIPE FOR LOVE Michelle
- 88 ☐ WINGED VICTORY Trevor
- 89 ☐ TIME FOR TOMORROW Ross
- 90 ☐ WILD FLIGHT Roszel

SILHOUETTE DESIRE, Department SD/6
1230 Avenue of the Americas
New York, NY 10020

Please send me the books I have checked above. I am enclosing $_____
(please add 50¢ to the cover postage and handling. NYS and NYC residents please add appropriate sales tax.) Send check or money order—no cash or C.O.D.'s please. Allow six weeks for delivery.

NAME _____

ADDRESS _____

CITY _____ STATE/ZIP _____

Get 6 new Silhouette Special Editions every month for a 15-day FREE trial!

Free Home Delivery, Free Previews, Free Bonus Books. Silhouette Special Editions are a new kind of romance novel. These are big, powerful stories that will capture your imagination. They're longer, with fully developed characters and intricate plots that will hold you spellbound from the first page to the very last.

Each month we will send you six exciting *new* Silhouette Special Editions, just as soon as they are published. If you enjoy them as much as we think you will, pay the invoice enclosed with your shipment. **They're delivered right to your door with never a charge for postage or handling, and there's no obligation to buy anything at any time.** To start receiving Silhouette Special Editions regularly, mail the coupon below today.

Silhouette Special Edition